THE NEW BASIC READERS

CURRICULUM FOUNDATION SERIES

REG U.S. PAT OFF.

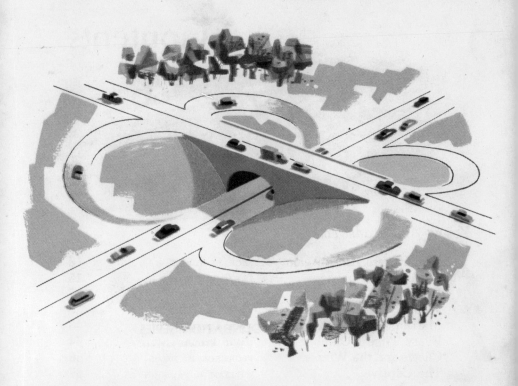

THE NEW

People and Progress

William S. Gray, Marion Monroe,

A. Sterl Artley, May Hill Arbuthnot

SCOTT, FORESMAN AND COMPANY

Chicago Atlanta Dallas Palo Alto Fair Lawn, N. J.

Contents

Young Americans Today

Early Adventures in Progress

Man-made Wonders of Today

Fun and Fancy

3

Young Americans Today

Paul Revere Rides Again

"A horse?" asked Mr. Crane. "What's all this talk about a horse?"

He set down his cup and looked inquiringly at his family gathered around the breakfast table.

Nelson, the younger of the Crane boys, choked with excitement and became speechless. He had rehearsed to himself many times just how he would make his request. But now that the moment had actually come, he was tongue-tied.

His brother John came boldly to his rescue.

"Nelson wants to rent Mr. Bugbee's old white horse," John explained to his father. "He wants to be Paul Revere in the parade, but he can't do that very well without a horse."

"Parade?" asked Mr. Crane. "What parade?"

"Nonsense, dear," said his wife. "Don't pretend you haven't heard of the Fourth of July parade. Our children have talked about nothing else for a week. It's to be a historical parade. Each child is to dress like a famous character in American history. Nelson's choice is Paul Revere. So he wants to rent Mr. Bugbee's horse."

"It—it—it's only five dollars," Nelson stammered. "Mr. Bugbee said I could have the horse all day for that. The price includes a saddle and a bridle, too. And I'll pay it out of my pocket money."

Mr. Crane stared thoughtfully at his son. "You think you know how to ride?"

"Yes, I do," Nelson assured him. "I've been practicing."

Mr. Crane glanced at his wife, who smiled and nodded. "Go ahead, my boy," he said. "But be careful."

John looked doubtful. When he was alone with Nelson, he said, "When did you learn to ride? I don't believe you can."

"I can ride *this* horse. Mr. Bugbee let me try the other day, and I didn't fall off even once. It's really a beautiful horse—or it will be with a little fixing up."

John smiled his big-brother smile. "Let's have a look at this wonderful horse," he said.

Old Mr. Bugbee was the village odd-job man. He sharpened lawn mowers, mended broken furniture, and trimmed hedges. He lived on the edge of the village, and his horse Buster roamed at will in a nearby pasture. The two boys found Mr. Bugbee leaning on the pasture fence, watching Buster.

"That's a lot of horse," John said critically.

Nelson swallowed hard. "But he acts friendly."

"That horse is as gentle as a kitten," bragged Mr. Bugbee. "He knows the route of the parade as well as you do. Buster and I used to deliver milk in that part of town. Ride him, Nelson. Show how you can handle him."

Mr. Bugbee and John boosted Nelson onto the old horse's broad back.

Grabbing Buster's mane, Nelson said, "Get up."
Buster took a step, stopped, and fell into a doze.

Nelson beamed. "What did I tell you?" he cried.
"Isn't this horse nice and gentle?"

"Well, let's take him home and see what we can
do with him," John said. Their arrival with Buster
on the end of a halter drew out the entire family.

"Isn't he something?" Nelson asked proudly.

"Quite a museum piece," commented Mr. Crane.

"But you said it was a white horse," protested
the boys' sister, Mary.

"A lot you know about horses," Nelson said in
a huff. "Wait till he's cleaned up. You'll see!"

"Of course we will," Mrs. Crane said soothingly.
"We'll all be proud of Nelson. You boys clean up
Buster. I'll see about getting Nelson's costume."

Undoubtedly the horse had not been bathed or
curried for years. Nelson and John gave him a
bath, using the garden hose, three bars of soap,
and a scrubbing brush. After he was dry, they
combed out his mane and tail. Nelson gazed at the
results of their work with pride. To him, Buster
looked like a horse cut from pure white marble.

Soon after lunch the bands, floats, and marchers
began to gather at one end of the village. Everyone applauded when Buster appeared. On his back
sat Paul Revere, looking much like Nelson Crane.
He was wearing a wig and a three-cornered hat.

"Splendid!" exclaimed Mr. Carpenter, the school principal. "You are our only horseman, Nelson. You shall lead the procession."

Buster jogged slowly to the head of the column. Whistles blew, and the school band blared out a stirring march. The parade was ready to start!

"There!" Nelson whispered in the horse's ear. "You're going to be a big hit!"

Buster started out briskly. He even pranced a little as the parade turned into Main Street.

And then it happened! In Buster's muddled old head Main Street meant milk to be delivered. He made his remembered first stop at the Spearmans' house. There he waited for the usual time it had taken Mr. Bugbee to carry in the bottles. Frenzied urging from Nelson had no effect.

10

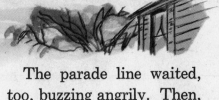

The parade line waited, too, buzzing angrily. Then, as unexpectedly as he had stopped, Buster started to jog off again. Behind him the paraders fell into step, and the band played with renewed liveliness.

At Dr. Fiddler's house the horse halted again.

Paraders and spectators tugged at Buster's bridle, shoved from the rear, and offered Nelson all sorts of humorous advice. But the old horse stood as if glued to the spot until habit told him to go on.

The third time that Buster stopped, the principal lost patience. "March around that horse!" he commanded. "We can't wait any longer. This is a parade, not a milk delivery!"

As the marching column detoured around Buster, Nelson's cheeks flamed. He heard the giggles of his fellow paraders. He gritted his teeth, clenched his fists, and suffered in silence. It seemed as if the parade would never pass.

But finally the last float rolled past the disgraced horseman. He and Buster were alone on an empty street. Buster drowsed.

Nelson was in the depths of depression. "Oh, Buster!" he cried. "How could you?"

11

Just then Nelson saw his brother running down the street. "For goodness' sake, hurry up," John panted. "You'll miss the whole show."

"Just try hurrying this old fool," Nelson moaned.

"Then get off and walk!" John cried impatiently.

Almost overcome with his disgrace, Nelson said bitterly, "Whoever heard of Paul Revere walking! People will laugh at me the rest of my life."

"Look!" John cried. "Here comes Mr. Bugbee. Maybe he can get Buster started."

But Mr. Bugbee was more interested in Buster's extraordinary cleverness than in Nelson's troubles.

"Imagine Buster remembering that milk route all these years!" he marveled. "I tell you, that horse is surely smart."

The clanging of the village fire bell interrupted Mr. Bugbee. Buster, too, heard that loud alarm. His nostrils quivered. His old eyes brightened.

A scarlet fire truck swung into Main Street. It went roaring past with siren screaming, headed for a burning shack along the river.

The bridle was jerked from Mr. Bugbee's hand as Buster lunged forward, uttering a shrill whinny. He was off like an antelope, with Nelson clinging to his back for dear life.

"Oh, my!" groaned Mr. Bugbee. "I forgot all about that fire bell. When Buster was just a young fellow, he belonged to the village fire department.

He has never forgotten that fire bell. He starts to gallop every time he hears it."

Up the street raced the fire truck. Behind it charged Mr. Bugbee's wonder horse. Lying flat, with his arms around Buster's neck, rode Nelson. His three-cornered hat blew off and hung by the strings tied beneath his chin. The pigtail of his wig streamed straight out behind.

The paraders scattered to let the fire truck pass. Before they could form ranks again, the unruly steed went clattering past with Nelson still astride it.

Desperately Nelson's hands groped for the flapping reins and froze onto them. He yanked hard and yelped, "Whoa!" To his intense amazement the horse slowed down.

Buster was no longer the sturdy young horse he had been in his fire-department days. His lungs wheezed like an old bellows, and his knees wobbled with exhaustion. The fire truck was out of sight now. The siren had ceased its deafening wail.

The old horse had slowed down to a trot, and at last Nelson managed to catch his breath. The boy felt bruised and sore from top to toe. His head whirled. But he and Buster were again leading the parade, for all the marchers had fallen in behind them. Nelson jerked his wig straight, slammed on his hat, wiped his steaming brow, and tucked in his shirt tail.

As the parade drew near the reviewing platform, Nelson could see people standing and waving. He heard whoops and cries of encouragement amid the thundering applause.

"Three cheers for Buster!"

"Three cheers for Paul Revere!"

"Three cheers for Nelson Crane!"

Nelson Crane looked straight ahead, an elated grin on his face. He swelled out his chest, pulled in his stomach, and tried to look every inch a hero as he led the parade into the park.

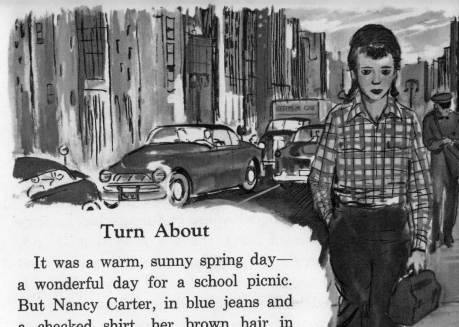

Turn About

It was a warm, sunny spring day—
a wonderful day for a school picnic.
But Nancy Carter, in blue jeans and
a checked shirt, her brown hair in
braids, scuffed along reluctantly with
her lunch box in her hand. She did
not want to go on a school picnic.

"But you'll have fun," her mother
had insisted at breakfast. "You like
to be in the country, Nancy."

Of course she liked the country. She had liked
living in the country. But four months ago her
family had moved to the city where her father was
to teach botany. Since then she had not felt happy.

Nancy did not like the city. She did not like
the rows and rows of apartment buildings. She
could scarcely draw a deep breath without smelling
the exhaust fumes of the cars that constantly
streamed past their apartment. Every time she
had to cross a city street, she felt terrified.

When the girls at school had learned that Nancy did not know which way was downtown and which was uptown, they were amazed. And when they had found out that she was too frightened to travel by herself in the subway, they had simply hooted— especially Evelyn Barns and Jessie Patterson.

So this morning when her mother packed Nancy's lunch and urged her to have a good time, Nancy just shrugged. She certainly wouldn't have a good time today. How could she when the other girls just stared at her or ignored her altogether?

When Nancy got to school, the picnic bus was at the door. The boys crowded into the back, pushing and shouting. They had their bats and balls with them and were already dividing into teams for a baseball game. The girls followed, choosing special partners to sit beside.

Nancy and the two teachers, Miss Howard and Miss Peck, were last. Miss Howard sat next to Nancy.

"Well, Nancy," she said, "isn't it a glorious day to be going to the country?"

"Yes, indeed," Nancy murmured politely. But she really did not care. She was wishing that one of the girls had grabbed her hand and said, "You sit by me."

Nancy put her hands in her pockets and stared out the window. She spoke only when the teacher addressed a remark to her.

16

For what seemed a long time to Nancy, the bus rolled past tall apartment houses not much different from the one she lived in. Then the bus turned left across a bridge and was soon out of the crowded city.

Again the bus turned, this time to the right, and went rolling smoothly up a broad highway. After a while, as she saw more and more wooded areas, Nancy began to relax. Perhaps she would have a good time, after all.

Finally the bus left the highway and turned into a shady road. When it stopped under a grove of trees, the youngsters piled out and stretched their legs. Immediately Miss Howard began helping the boys organize their baseball game. The bus driver offered to be umpire, and the game got under way.

"Now what do you girls want to do?" asked Miss Howard.

"Explore!" Evelyn Barns spoke up. "That's what we did last year."

"Oh, yes, let's explore!" the other girls joined in enthusiastically.

"All right," said Miss Howard. "I'll stay with the boys, and Miss Peck can accompany you girls. Only don't go too far."

"Well, let's get started, girls," said Miss Peck. "Here's a well-marked trail. Let's try it and see where it leads us."

Nancy strolled along behind the rest into the thick, shady woods. A thrush sang joyously in a bush, and a frisky chipmunk skipped about among lovely white trilliums. Nearby a little stream flowed lazily along. Presently the trail opened into a clearing.

From a beech tree at the far edge of the clearing came a call, "Chewink! Chewink!"

Startled, Evelyn asked, "What's that?"

"A chewink," said Nancy, almost automatically. Then she felt embarrassed. Would the others think she was showing off her knowledge? "There's the bird in that tree," she added bashfully.

The girls gazed with interest at the tree to which Nancy pointed, but they managed only to glimpse the bird in swift flight.

Miss Peck noticed their interest and said with a smile, "Perhaps Nancy could tell us the names of some of these trees and wild flowers, too."

Evelyn asked at once, "What are those red-and-yellow flowers with the long stems?"

"Columbines," Nancy informed them.

"Look at that tree with three different kinds of leaves on it!" cried Jessie. "What is that?"

There was a silence as the girls automatically turned to Nancy for an answer.

"Sassafras tree," Nancy told them. "Isn't that a lovely-sounding name?"

The other girls went on up the trail, but Evelyn and Jessie waited to walk beside Nancy.

"Where did you learn so much about the woods?" Jessie asked.

"My father teaches botany," Nancy said. "When he taught school in our country town, I used to go on field trips with his classes sometimes."

Evelyn pointed to a bush about thirty feet from the trail. "Do you know what that bush is?" she asked.

"I think it's a spicebush," Nancy replied. "Let's go and see." Leaving the trail, they went over to the bush. Nancy crushed some of the leaves and smelled them.

"Yes, that's what it is," she said. "The leaves have a spicy odor, like citronella."

Nancy was now so absorbed in looking for other familiar plants that she led the two girls farther and farther into the woods. Finally Jessie panted, "I'm tired. Let's rest a minute."

Nancy looked around, smiling contentedly. "It's so quiet here, I could stay forever," she thought. Then suddenly she caught her breath and listened intently. It was *too* quiet. Why didn't they hear the rest of the group talking? Surely they wouldn't all have stopped at once.

"Where did the others go?" she asked abruptly.

Jessie and Evelyn looked about in dismay.

"Why, where's the trail?" Evelyn cried, fear in her voice.

"Let's yell," suggested Nancy. "Miss Peck!" she shouted. "Yoo-hoo! Wait for us!"

There was silence except for the "Cheep! Cheep!" of a young bird.

"Miss Peck!" all three girls shouted. "Here we are, Miss Peck."

Again there was no reply.

"We must be lost," Evelyn whimpered.

Nancy was impatient with the frightened girls.

"Don't be silly," she said. "We're not lost yet. We'll head for the trail and find the others."

"But which way is the trail?" Evelyn asked.

"It's over that way," said Nancy, pointing to her left.

"No!" contradicted Jessie, on the edge of panic. "It's that way, to the right."

Suddenly Nancy felt completely mixed up. "All right," she said. "Let's go Jessie's way."

They started off. But instead of finding the trail, they headed into thicker and thicker brush. Jessie grabbed Evelyn's arm. Evelyn was pale with fear. Her face crumpled, and she began to cry.

Nancy remembered how the girls had called her "Fraidy Cat" because she was scared of the subway and of city traffic. "Turn about is fair play," she thought. Then, laughing at the girls, she said, "Don't be such babies. We'll get back all right."

"But how will we find the trail?" Evelyn sobbed.

All at once she uttered a shriek of terror and sprang back. "A snake!"

"For goodness' sake!" Nancy cried scornfully when she saw where Evelyn's trembling finger was pointing. "It's just a harmless garter snake."

"Well, how would I know that?" Evelyn said indignantly. "I'm not used to snakes."

Nancy flushed, feeling ashamed of herself. Turn about was *not* fair play if it meant hurting someone's feelings. "Don't cry, Evelyn," she soothed. "The main thing is not to get scared."

Evelyn wiped her eyes and attempted to smile. Jessie gave a long, quivering sigh. "Can you get us back to the others?" she asked.

"Oh, sure," Nancy declared cheerfully, hoping to inspire confidence.

Nancy recalled what her father had once told her on a long hike in the woods. "Get your directions from the sun or wind if you can," he had said.

She looked up. The dense foliage shut out the sun, and there was no wind. She tried to recognize some tree or bush that she had seen earlier on their hike. Suddenly she became aware of the green moss on the tree trunks. Most of the trees had the green coloring only on one side.

Jumping up energetically from the log where she had been sitting, Nancy cried, "Let's go! I think I can get us back to the trail. We must go east."

"But how will we know which direction is east?" asked the girls.

Nancy pointed to some nearby trees. "Do you see that green moss growing on the side of those trees? Well, my father told me that sometimes in a deep woods small plants like these will grow only on the north side of a tree. It isn't always true. But if you see moss on only one side of a number of trees, that side is probably north."

"How does that help us?" Jessie asked forlornly.

Nancy picked up a stick and began drawing lines on the ground. "We went north when we started from school," she explained. "We turned left to go across the bridge, so then we were going west. After we crossed the bridge, we turned right and rode north along a highway. We turned west off the highway. Then when we reached that wooded place, we turned off to the right. That means we were facing north when we stopped."

The other girls gazed earnestly at Nancy's map as she continued, "The trail we took went right on north. But we turned left off the trail to look at the spicebush. So now we're west of the trail. To get back to it, we just have to go in the opposite direction."

"Then let's hurry east as fast as we can," said Evelyn. "My, you're smart," she added, her voice full of admiration.

"I will be if we can manage to keep going in one direction," Nancy replied with a laugh. "But that's awfully hard to do in the woods. We'd better walk toward something we can identify. Let's try to keep that tall birch tree up ahead in view."

The girls started eastward with Nancy leading. The going was rough. They stumbled over roots and stones. Thorny branches caught at them.

"Ouch!" Jessie exclaimed. "I got a bad scratch that time." She wiped the blood off her bare leg.

"How silly of her to wear her jeans rolled up in the woods!" Nancy thought. But she helped Jessie tie her handkerchief around the scratch, and they trudged on.

Suddenly Nancy halted. "Sh!" she commanded.

Evelyn and Jessie obediently stood still. A low, gurgling noise could be heard.

"A brook!" Nancy cried. "Remember? There was a brook beside the trail!"

24

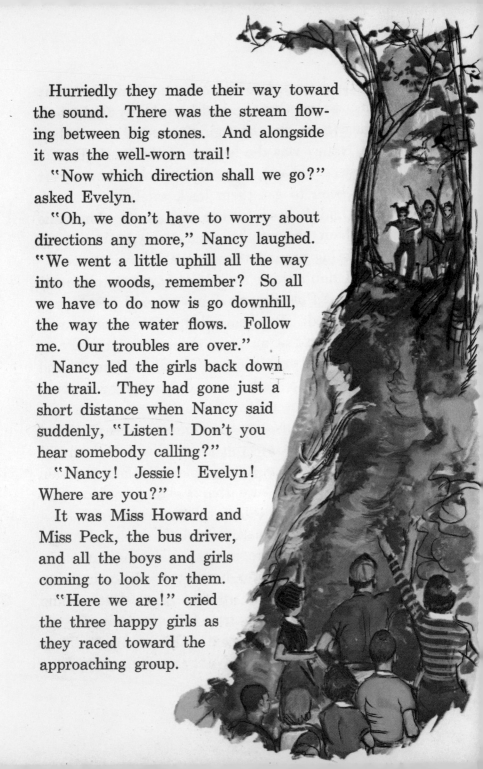

Hurriedly they made their way toward the sound. There was the stream flowing between big stones. And alongside it was the well-worn trail!

"Now which direction shall we go?" asked Evelyn.

"Oh, we don't have to worry about directions any more," Nancy laughed. "We went a little uphill all the way into the woods, remember? So all we have to do now is go downhill, the way the water flows. Follow me. Our troubles are over."

Nancy led the girls back down the trail. They had gone just a short distance when Nancy said suddenly, "Listen! Don't you hear somebody calling?"

"Nancy! Jessie! Evelyn! Where are you?"

It was Miss Howard and Miss Peck, the bus driver, and all the boys and girls coming to look for them.

"Here we are!" cried the three happy girls as they raced toward the approaching group.

"What happened to you?" cried Miss Peck. It was easy to see that she had been badly frightened.

Among them, the three girls managed to tell their story. Nancy was the heroine of the tale. Evelyn and Jessie could not stop talking about how clever she had been to get them back safely.

"If it hadn't been for her and all the things she knows about the woods," said Evelyn, "we'd still be wandering around there. We'd have starved!"

"Oh, I don't think so," Miss Howard comforted the girls. "I'm sure we'd have found you before that happened. But remember this experience and next time don't stray from the marked trail."

"I'll remember all right," said Evelyn. "And I'll remember to walk close to Nancy. She could find her way out of any place."

For a moment Nancy was tempted to say, "Turn about, Evelyn. Now you know how I felt when I was frightened in a strange place." But she said nothing. She was sure that Evelyn would understand her feelings now.

They all headed back toward the bus and lunch. Afterwards there were games and races, and then it was time to start for home. As the youngsters rushed aboard the bus to find seats, Evelyn and Jessie grasped Nancy's arms affectionately.

"Sit by us," they begged. "Please!"

"I'd love to," replied Nancy, smiling happily.

Dark Horse

The minute I saw the notice of the *Evening News* spelling contest on the bulletin board, I knew who would win. Who? Dick Buckmaster, of course.

Dick is my best friend, but that had nothing to do with my picking him to win the spelling contest. I mean that boy has brains! He doesn't even have to study. Show him a page from a history book. He skims over it, and immediately he knows it. It's the same with arithmetic and science, and especially with spelling.

You'd think that Dick would have won a lot of contests, but he hasn't. The way I figure it is that he's never won a contest because he's never tried. He has the brains all right, but no push.

I decided that this time things would be different. This time Dick couldn't help winning because he'd have *his* brains and *me* to push him.

After school I, Willie Clinton, told him, "You're going to win that spelling contest, Dick."

"O.K.," he said absent-mindedly. "How about going down to Crystal Creek this afternoon for a little fishing, Willie?"

"We'll go fishing," I agreed. "But we'll take a spelling book with us."

"What for?" asked Dick. "I know all the words in that book backward and forward."

Well, Dick had a point there. So I went to our teacher, Miss Butterfield, and asked for a list of extra-hard words.

"Why, Willie," she remarked, looking surprised. "Are you going to compete for the prize?"

It's no wonder she acted surprised. When I get an A in spelling, it's time to declare a holiday.

"No," I replied. "But I'm going to coach Dick Buckmaster. It's a cinch Dick'll win the contest. He's a champion speller. But all champions have a coach and go into training before a big match. I figured that's what Dick should do, and I'm going to be his coach."

"You're absolutely right," said Miss Butterfield. "Take this list of One Hundred Spelling Demons. Some are sure to be used in the contest."

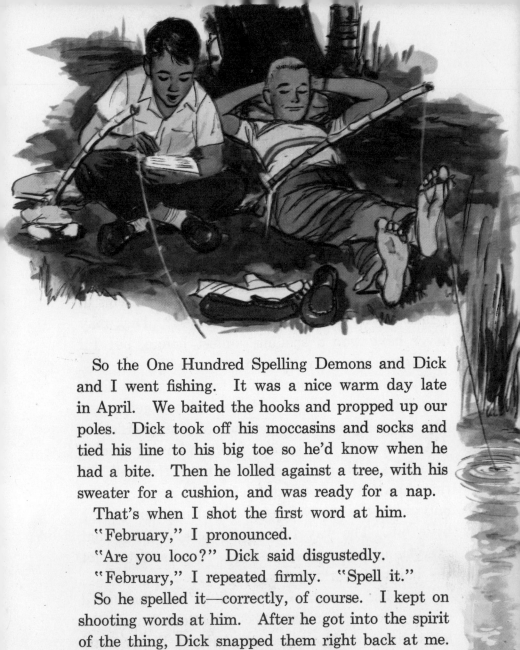

So the One Hundred Spelling Demons and Dick
and I went fishing. It was a nice warm day late
in April. We baited the hooks and propped up our
poles. Dick took off his moccasins and socks and
tied his line to his big toe so he'd know when he
had a bite. Then he lolled against a tree, with his
sweater for a cushion, and was ready for a nap.

That's when I shot the first word at him.

"February," I pronounced.

"Are you loco?" Dick said disgustedly.

"February," I repeated firmly. "Spell it."

So he spelled it—correctly, of course. I kept on
shooting words at him. After he got into the spirit
of the thing, Dick snapped them right back at me.
It was a cinch he'd win that contest.

The next day word got around school that I had
said Dick would win the spelling contest. Before
long everyone was arguing about it.

More than half the class thought that Nora Law
had the best chance. Nora can spell all right, and
she's a hard worker, too. No one really wanted
her to win because she always gloats about how
smart she is. Almost all the kids hoped that Dick
would win. But they doubted that he would try
hard enough.

"Well," I told them, "a dark horse often wins in
a race. Why not in a spelling contest? Dick may
never have won a spelling contest before, but I'll
guarantee he's going to win this one."

That put the responsibility for seeing that Dick
won squarely up to me. So each day I got a new
and tougher list of words from Miss Butterfield.

After a week of coaching I began having trouble
with Dick. He got tired of working. He's tall and
thin, and just to look at Dick you'd never get the
impression that he was lazy. But I'm afraid he is a
little bit. The way I figure it, he's so smart that
everything seems easy to him. So he never got
the habit of working for things.

"I've had enough of this spelling," he announced
one evening. "I'm through." He tossed aside the
latest list of hard words, called Brain Teasers, and
started to amble off.

"Hey, wait!" I shouted. "I'm responsible for seeing that you win. My reputation is at stake!"

"What do I care about that?" he called over his shoulder.

I coaxed desperately, "The whole class is behind you. I guaranteed you'd win."

Dick groaned. "You shouldn't make promises for me."

"Be reasonable," I persisted. "If you quit now, you'll waste all the work you've already done."

That did it. Dick hated to think of any work of his going to waste. So I kept on giving him words to spell, and he kept on spelling them. But I was afraid his heart wasn't in it. Once I said, "Boo!" just to startle him.

He said sleepily, "That's spelled b-o-o."

It was now getting pretty close to the date of the contest. One morning I came to school and found a new notice on the bulletin board. The *Evening News* was making a big thing of this contest. Besides a fine new dictionary for each room winner, there was to be a ten-dollar prize for each school winner.

The best speller in the whole town would get a trip to the State capital. There he would compete against winners from all over the State. The final winner would go to Washington, where he would meet the President of the United States.

The day finally came when we were to take the
first test. It was on a Wednesday. Everyone in
our room had to enter the contest, although I considered it a waste of time for all of us but Nora
and Dick. This first test would whittle our class
down to the ten best spellers. The ten would then
take another test to find the room winner.

Barney Dana sat in front of me. Apparently he
had no hope of winning a dictionary. He was wig-
gling and squirming and chewing his pencil. After
the teacher had pronounced *exaggerate, counselor,
chamois,* and *allegiance,* Barney
laid down his pencil.

The results of this test showed that Dick was one of the first ten, naturally. So was Nora. So, for a wonder, was I.

The following Friday we—the ten best spellers—went into the gym for the room finals. Ten desks had been put in there, and we all took our places nervously. What a test that was! There wasn't a word in it, though, that I hadn't drilled Dick on.

On Monday I was at school bright and early. I could hardly wait to find out if Dick was the room winner. But Miss Butterfield shut up like a clam. She wouldn't tell me.

"Please say if Dick won," I begged.

She only laughed. "It's no use, Willie. I'm going to announce it to the class as a whole. Mrs. Shearer, the principal, is coming in to present the dictionary to the winner."

We were all very quiet when the principal came in. For once Dick was sitting up as straight as his front hair. Nora Law was leaning back in her seat, looking calm and sure of herself.

As for me, I couldn't even pretend to be calm. I sat on the edge of my seat and held my breath.

Miss Butterfield announced, "Mrs. Shearer and pupils, we have a big surprise. The room spelling contest has been won by a dark horse."

A dark horse! That *could* be Dick.

"The winner," she said, "is Willie Clinton."

I was stunned. Everybody was laughing and clapping, and Dick was pounding my back.

"After all," he said, "you did all the work. The next time I'll teach you, and then *I'll* win."

Well, here I am in the State capital. I'll never know how I won the school and city contests, too, unless it's the way the principal figured it out. When she congratulated me, she said, "How did you become such a good speller, Willie?"

"He's been coaching another boy," put in Miss Butterfield.

"It always works," said the principal. "If you want to learn something well, teach it to someone else."

Well, it's worked so far. Now I'm going to find another contestant who wants coaching in spelling. I'd like to shake hands with the President.

Who's Scared of Bears?

It was Don Brown who had suggested the idea.
If Bill Jenkins, the new boy in town, wanted to join
the Centerville Detective Club, he must pass a test
to prove his courage. Now the five club members
were meeting to decide what the test would be. It
did not take them long. A trip after dark to a deserted shack in Bear Swamp would be perfect.

That evening the shack was prepared for Bill's
trial. A collection of fireflies was brought in from
the woods. Their tiny, flickering lights made mysterious bright spots against the dark planks of the
walls. Huge bats were cut from black paper. An
old stuffed owl and a cardboard skeleton added a
ghostly look to the scene.

"It's really spooky," Don chuckled. "And this
skeleton left from my Halloween party
is the spookiest thing of all."

The skeleton was suspended from a beam by a string. When the door was opened, a draft would cause the skeleton to sway as if it were walking. An oatmeal container with twelve marbles in it was attached to the door by a cord. Opening the door would push the container along the floor. Then the marbles rolling about would produce a ghostly rattle guaranteed to chill anyone's bones.

Under a bunk in a corner of the shack the boys hid a carved wooden box wrapped in a gunny sack. The new boy was to find the box and take it back to the club room as proof that he had been there.

Bill Jenkins had already been told that he would be accepted as a club member if he passed a test to show that he had the courage needed by a good detective. Now the boys hurried back to town to tell Bill to meet them the next morning in their club room, the Browns' garage, for his instructions.

When the new boy appeared, Claude Spencer, the club president, told him what to do. "You must go alone to an old shack in Bear Swamp after dark tonight. A little carved box is hidden there. You must bring it back to the club room and give it to us. You know where Bear Swamp is, don't you?"

"Yes, I know. It's out on Cedar Mills Road," Bill said. But he looked troubled.

"You aren't scared to go out to that old shack after dark, are you?" Claude jeered.

"I—I guess not," Bill
faltered. "But do bears
really prowl around there?"

Claude and Don exchanged amused glances.

"Oh, not many," said Don casually. "Sometimes
a few *do* come down to eat huckleberries."

"A man met a bear at the edge of the swamp one
day," Jim Dyer remarked. He omitted explaining
that this incident had occurred ten years ago.

"There won't be any bears in the old shack,"
Ted Fanning said. "And if you do meet one on the
trail up the creek—well, you're smart enough to
figure out a way to escape, aren't you?"

"A detective must be smart," Stan Jones added.
"But maybe you'd rather not join our club."

Bill Jenkins gulped. But he said, "Sure I want
to join. Who's scared of bears?"

So matters were settled. At eight o'clock that night Bill was to make his solitary journey to the shack. He was to obtain the box and bring it to the club room that same night.

"He'll think he's run into something worse than a bear when he sees those fireflies lighting up that skeleton," Ted said smugly. "I'd give a dollar to see the expression on Bill's face."

Jim slapped his knee. "Why shouldn't we see him?" he asked. "Why not go out and hide in the bushes near the shack? We can look through the window and see the whole show."

"That's a good idea," Don agreed. "Besides, if Bill gets too scared, we can just go and keep him company. We'll tell him it's only a joke."

By seven o'clock that evening the club members were heading toward the old shack. They wanted plenty of time to be there ahead of Bill. On their arrival they hid in some bushes not far from the shack and waited for Bill to appear.

To the eager boys the wait seemed endless. The last rays of sunlight faded. Soon the evening star glowed bright and clear above the murmuring reeds in Bear Swamp.

"Won't Bill ever get here?" Ted muttered.

"Maybe he isn't coming," Stan suggested.

"But he said he'd come, and he seemed anxious to get into the club," Ted whispered back.

Minutes passed. The moon had risen and was shining above the shadowy fir trees. Bored with waiting, the five watchers peered from their hiding places. The woods were very dark now and full of weird noises.

At last there came a sharp crackling of twigs. "He's coming!" Claude whispered hoarsely.

They strained their eyes to see the approaching figure. Suddenly Ted gripped Stan's arm hard.

"Look! Wh-what is it?" he stuttered.

For a moment Stan was too startled to answer. Then he gasped, "It's—it's a bear!"

It certainly was a huge black furry form waddling clumsily through the tall grass. In the moonlight the boys could see bright yellow eyes and a mouth full of white teeth. The bear turned its head this way and that as if scenting the evening air. Then it advanced toward the clump of bushes where the boys were hiding.

"Come on, fellows!" Stan croaked. "It's coming right at us!" He turned to flee and collided with Claude. As the boys raced pell-mell to the shack, Ted tripped over a tree root, and Jim sprawled awkwardly on top of him.

Somehow all five boys managed to tumble inside the shack and slam the door. Ted got to his feet and peeked out the window.

"The bear's going away," he reported in relief. "I guess all that racket scared it."

For a few minutes after the bear had disappeared, the boys huddled together in the shack. Then they opened the door with caution and peered out.

"Whew! I'm glad it's gone," Ted said.

"There's no use waiting for Bill any longer," Jim spoke up hurriedly. "I guess he isn't coming."

Without another word the five conspirators bolted for home.

The next morning the boys met at the club room to discuss Bill's failure to appear at the deserted shack. Inside the door they found the carved box. There was a note under it saying:

Can you fellows come up to my house Saturday afternoon to try out my new airplane model? There will be some chocolate pie.

Bill Jenkins

The boys looked at one another in amazement.

"So Bill did go out to the shack after all," Ted said in an awed voice. "I don't suppose he saw the bear, though."

No one mentioned the plot that they had hatched to frighten Bill. But the boys agreed unanimously to accept his invitation.

When they arrived at Bill's house, they blinked
in surprise at an object lying before the living-room
hearth. It was a bearskin rug with yellow glass
eyes, a red mouth, and long white teeth.

"You don't suppose——" Ted whispered haltingly.
"You don't suppose Bill and that rug——"

Don stooped and picked up something from the
rug. It was a dry pine needle. There was also a
slight smudge of swamp mud on a hind claw. The
five detectives looked a trifle shamefaced as the
same thought occurred to each of them. A boy on
all fours with a bearskin rug over his back might
be mistaken for a real bear—in the moonlight.

"And we wondered how smart Bill is!" Claude
said. "He's smart enough for our club any day!"

Bill, who had followed the boys into the room,
said with a grin, "You're pretty smart detectives
yourselves. I'm proud to join your club."

Martha Wasn't Musical

"One and two, three-ee, fo-ur," Martha chanted as she practiced her new piano piece. Her music teacher would not come till next Thursday, but she wanted to be note-perfect by Tuesday. Then she could devote all of Wednesday's practice period to what she called "putting in the expression."

"One and two-oo, three-ee, fo-ur," she counted, thumping vigorously. "One and two-oo——"

"Dig and do-oo," teased her older brother Victor from the dining room, where he was supposed to be doing his homework. "Do you call that music?" He grinned as he put both hands over his ears to deaden the sound of Martha's playing.

Martha considered Victor a musical genius. He could play almost any musical instrument a little, but he played the flute especially well. He was a member of the high-school orchestra, and he also played with his parents in their home concerts.

Martha's highest ambition was to accompany her father's clarinet, her mother's violin, and Victor's flute. But she despaired of ever playing the piano well enough to achieve her goal. Everybody said that Martha wasn't musical.

"Are you going to keep on hitting those keys so hard?" Victor called. "Or is it safe to uncover my ears now?"

As Martha was about to answer Victor's teasing, something caught her eye. She pointed to a gray coat on a chair across the room. "Is Aunt Jane here?" she asked.

"Yes," replied Victor, "she and Mother are out in the garden." Glancing out the window, he added, "They're coming in now."

"Oh, mercy!" Martha sprang up. "I'm going to run. If Aunt Jane sees me at the piano, she'll make me play for her."

But it was too late. The front door opened, and the two women came in. Aunt Jane turned to Martha. "How do you do, my dear?" she said. "And how are your piano lessons going? You must play something for me."

44

The girl glanced appealingly at her mother. As usual, her mother looked worried at the mention of Martha's piano playing. But she gave her daughter a nod of encouragement and said, "Yes, play your pretty new piece for us, dear."

Dutifully Martha sat down at the piano. She saw Victor grinning wickedly at her. But at least he wasn't walking out of the room with his hands over his ears.

Conscientiously she went through the composition. When she finished playing, Aunt Jane rose to go. "Thank you very much, Martha," she said. "You keep excellent time."

Martha's mother brightened. "Yes, dear," she said. "Your sense of rhythm is very good indeed. Why, there's no telling what musical ability you may develop when you're a bit older."

As the three others left the room, Martha looked a bit sad. There was just one occasion when she played to everyone's satisfaction. That was when the children marched in for weekly assembly-hall programs. Usually an older girl played. But at the beginning of the second term Miss Thorpe had asked Martha to do it.

"You keep such good time," Miss Thorpe had said. "And your touch is firm. The children can follow your playing easily." Martha felt better as she thought of her teacher's words.

The next forenoon, school was proceeding in its regular fashion. The science lesson had just begun when suddenly there was a loud noise. From her desk Martha could see into the hall. The third-grade teacher, Miss Burrows, was running to the top of the stairs. In her classroom the children were beginning to get noisy.

Then the fire gong began to ring, one loud clang after another. Martha and her classmates got to their feet and started automatically to file out the rear door of their room. There was Miss Burrows again, this time running back to her pupils.

The hall seemed hazy. Surely that was smoke coming out of the heating register near the third-grade classroom! Some of the children halted and clutched one another in dismay. Many of them had younger brothers and sisters in the school. At the thought of danger to little Susan or Ann or Junior, they became panic-stricken and began to push and shove.

After years of fire drills to prepare for such an emergency, here was the real thing! Yet nobody remembered the meaning of the drill now.

Near Martha's classroom stood the piano used when the children marched into assembly. There had never been music for fire drill before, but now Miss Thorpe motioned Martha toward the piano.

"Play, Martha!" she ordered.

Martha obeyed at once. She opened the piano in her usual unhurried way and began playing her favorite march. Dozens of times the youngsters had marched along to its loud, regular beat. Its familiar rhythm began to calm the excited boys and girls.

The music actually seemed to be talking to them. "Have sense. Don't run. Pick up your feet and walk out. Don't push. Don't scream. You'll all get out if you don't rush."

Thump, thump! The music went on as steadily as the tick of a clock. Tramp, tramp, tramp went hundreds of feet in step.

Thump, thump! Tramp, tramp! Now another class was coming down the hall, heading for the fire escape. The youngsters were marching along in orderly fashion through the smoke. Their eyes were serious.

The smoke was getting much thicker now. From the registers came a deep, roaring sound, as if a huge beast were gnawing at the bars of his cage, growling to be set free. Then came the screams of sirens. The fire engines were on the way!

As Martha played steadily on, she felt strangely tired. Her eyes and throat ached from the smoke, and every now and then she coughed. If only she could stop playing! But she was afraid that the building was not yet emptied.

"Faster, Martha. Please play a little faster," Miss Thorpe whispered anxiously into the ear of the weary girl.

Obediently Martha quickened the time just a little. Thump, thump, thump, thump!

Now the fifth-grade class was coming down the hall. Suddenly Martha wanted to play furiously fast to get all the children out of the building and have it over. But she forced herself to remember that to go safely, they must not go too fast. They must not run. They must not trip. Instinctively the girl knew that the firm, regular beat of the music was their only safeguard.

By now Martha's eyes were smarting so badly that she had to shut them for a minute. When she opened them, the last boy and girl were filing out the fire-escape door. No one was behind them.

Then, although she could not remember that she had stopped playing, she knew that someone was carrying her. She was outside now and, oh, how it hurt to breathe! Dimly she heard men's voices and the sound of fire-engine motors.

That evening Martha was resting on the living-room sofa when her teacher came to ask how she was feeling.

"Martha was very brave," Miss Thorpe told the girl's family. "There would certainly have been a real panic if it hadn't been for Martha. Her playing marched the children out in order. She was our drum major!"

Martha's feat made more of an impression on Victor than on her parents. They seemed merely thankful that she was safe. But Victor had gone to see the scorched, smoke-blackened rooms and halls of Martha's school. He had also seen the debris in the basement, where the fire had started from a small explosion in the furnace.

Now he laughed to cover his shakiness at what might have happened if the children had stampeded to the fire escape, and to conceal his pride in what his sister had done.

"Miss Thorpe's right," he said. "Drum major is a good name for Martha. She always plays as if she were beating a drum. Mother, why not let her take drum lessons instead of piano?"

"Would you prefer drum lessons, Martha?" her mother asked.

The effects of the smoke made Martha feel as if she had a bad cold. But the thought of having a drum was cheering. "Oh, yes," she wheezed.

Before the week was over, Martha had acquired a big new bass drum and had begun lessons. She learned so rapidly that even the teacher was astonished at her progress.

Since Martha did so well with the bass drum, it was soon decided that she should learn to play a snare drum also. With two drums to beat time on, Martha was so happy that she could hardly contain herself. Her energetic practicing could be heard all over the neighborhood.

During the summer vacation Martha kept up her practicing industriously. Victor no longer covered his ears when he heard her musical efforts. He even seemed to enjoy listening to her.

The next autumn several exciting things happened to Martha. As soon as school began, she and her drums were taken into the school band. A short time later Martha found herself marching with the band in a parade. As she stepped along, beating her drum loudly, she thought happily that at last she was doing something she had always wanted to do.

Not long after this great event in Martha's life, there was a special school program at which the Mayor was the principal speaker. In his speech the Mayor praised the band's fine playing. Martha glowed with pride at this tribute to the band.

Then, at the end of his speech, the Mayor called Martha's name. When the surprised girl mounted the platform, the Mayor presented her with a medal for helping prevent a panic during the school fire. The audience applauded and cheered loudly as she stammered her thanks.

That evening Martha showed the medal to her family. "It doesn't say a thing about my playing," she said, sounding a little hurt.

Her mother and father and Victor all looked at the medal. On one side was Martha's name. On the other side were the words "For courage."

"Pretty keen!" crowed Victor.

Her father patted Martha's head in approval.

Her mother said proudly, "Oh, Martha, darling! It's a lovely medal."

"Ye-es," said Martha slowly, "but something else would be much nicer than a medal."

"Something else?" chorused the others.

Martha hesitated. Then she burst out in one breath, "Will you please let me play the drums in our family concerts now? That would be the best thing of all!"

"Come on, then," said her father, moving over to the piano. "I know a piece of music that will just suit us four. Let's see what we can do."

Every Time I Climb a Tree

Every time I climb a tree,
Every time I climb a tree,
Every time I climb a tree
I scrape a leg
Or skin a knee;
And every time I climb a tree
I find some ants
Or dodge a bee
And get the ants
All over me.

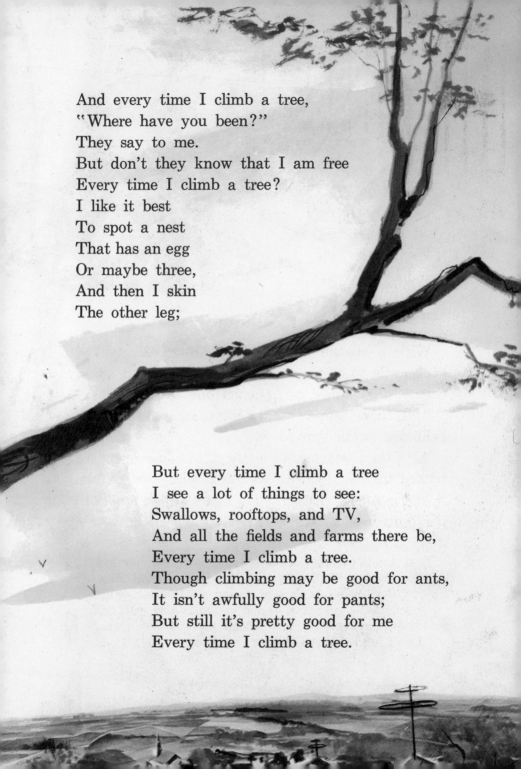

And every time I climb a tree,
"Where have you been?"
They say to me.
But don't they know that I am free
Every time I climb a tree?
I like it best
To spot a nest
That has an egg
Or maybe three,
And then I skin
The other leg;

But every time I climb a tree
I see a lot of things to see:
Swallows, rooftops, and TV,
And all the fields and farms there be,
Every time I climb a tree.
Though climbing may be good for ants,
It isn't awfully good for pants;
But still it's pretty good for me
Every time I climb a tree.

Cheers for the Winner

With a spatter of gravel, Chuck Evers braked his bicycle to a stop at the foot of the front steps. Coony, the family cat, opened one eye lazily.

"Hi, there, fellow," said Chuck, scratching Coony behind a battle-scarred ear.

As Chuck started to enter the house, he saw, tacked on the door, an envelope addressed to him in his mother's writing. He tore it open and read the note inside.

Dear Chuck,
    I couldn't reach you at the ball game to tell you that I'm rushing off to see your father in California for a few days before he is sent overseas. I've told your grandmother all about it, and you're to stay with her while I'm away. Sorry about the soapbox races. Don't forget to feed Coony.

Love,
Mother

Chuck stood looking at the note with a worried frown. The boy had known that his father, who was a navy officer, might be sent overseas soon. But now that his mother was away, what was he to do about the races?

The All-American Soap Box Derby was two days off. Brad, Chuck's fifteen-year-old brother, was one of the contestants, and for weeks Chuck had been counting on going to Akron, Ohio, to see the races.

Now Chuck's mother could not drive him there, as she had promised. Brad, who was already in Akron, was no help. Chuck knew that Gram could not go with him, but she might let him go on the train alone. He hurried off to ask her.

Chuck's grandmother was in her garden when he arrived. "No, Chuck," she said in answer to her grandson's request. "I'm responsible for you now that your family is away, and I can't allow you to go off alone that way."

"But, Gram," Chuck protested, "I'm eleven years old! I'll be all right on the train by myself."

"It isn't the train ride that bothers me," replied Gram. "It's your being alone in those enormous crowds in Akron. Something might happen to you, and Brad would be too busy to look after you."

At Chuck's look of bitter disappointment, Gram's eyes softened. "Maybe you can get a friend to go with you," she suggested. "I think that would be all right. If you can, I'll pay all the expenses for both of you."

"Thanks, Gram," said Chuck, his eyes sparkling. "I'll find someone right away."

Chuck ran inside to the telephone. Whom should he call? Nat Fox would not be back from camp till next week. Who else? Bud Wicks! Hurriedly he dialed Bud's number.

Mrs. Wicks answered. "Bud isn't here," she said. "He's driving to Chicago with his uncle."

"Oh." Chuck's disappointment was so evident that Mrs. Wicks asked him what was wrong.

After the boy had explained his problem, Mrs. Wicks clucked sympathetically. "Oh, dear, I wish I could help you. Why don't you try Sam Eaves? No, he's out of town now, too. What about Pidge Orway?"

Chuck hesitated. He had thought of Pidge, but for some reason Pidge had not been friendly lately. He had dropped in once or twice, mostly to try out Chuck's new bicycle, but each time he had avoided Brad. He might not even care about seeing Brad race. Still, in a pinch, maybe Pidge would go.

"Well, thanks, Mrs. Wicks," Chuck said finally. "I'll go over and talk to him."

Pidge was mowing the grass when Chuck rode up. "Hello, Pidge," called Chuck. "I want to ask you something."

Pidge stopped mowing and scowled. "What?" he asked suspiciously.

Once again Chuck explained his problem. "So how would you like to go to Akron with me? My grandmother said that she'd pay all the expenses if I could get someone. We can stay in the motel room my mother reserved."

"Well, why ask *me* to go?" asked Pidge with a shrug.

"There's no one else around," Chuck told him.

Pidge shook his head. "I'm not going. I don't want to see the Derby."

"Oh, come on," Chuck pleaded. "I just have to see Brad race. If he wins the Derby, he will get five thousand dollars for his college education. I'll let you ride my bike two days a week if you'll come."

Pidge stared. He had always wanted a bicycle, and he envied Chuck the beautiful brand-new model that Brad had won in the local soapbox races and given to his younger brother Chuck.

"O.K.," Pidge said finally. "It's a deal."

After Pidge had received his mother's consent to go, Chuck mounted his bicycle. "I'll tell Gram," he said, "and let you know what time we'll leave."

Early the next day the two boys left by train for Akron. During the ride Chuck chattered happily. "Let's go out to Derbytown to see Brad first thing. That's a camp near Akron where the fellows who are racing stay. It'll be fun to see what it's like. Besides, maybe we can do something for Brad."

Pidge had very little to say. Most of the time he stared gloomily out the window.

Meanwhile, in one of the cottages at Derbytown, Brad was talking earnestly with Mr. Rod Black of the *Bay City Times-Post*. This newspaper had sponsored the soapbox races in Brad's home town. The two were discussing a letter, signed "One Who Knows," that had been received yesterday by the Derby officials. It stated that Brad's father had helped Brad build his racer, and now the officials were challenging Brad's right to race.

The statement in the letter was not true, and it really hurt. Though Brad had said nothing about it, he was pretty sure that Pidge had written the letter because of something that had happened two months ago.

"Well, don't worry," said the newspaperman as he rose to leave the cottage. "The inspectors are fair, and they don't *want* to doubt your word. But there have been a few cases where the contestants have said they made their racers when they didn't. So the inspectors can't afford to overlook any hint of cheating. I'm sure, though, that you passed the test they gave you this morning at the trade school on using tools needed to build a racer."

"I hope so," Brad said soberly. Then he added more cheerfully, "I should have. I started making things with Dad's tools when I was six."

"Yes, they couldn't catch you on a single tool," laughed Mr. Black. "Well, I'll be back at three to take you to headquarters for the final decision."

Shortly before three, Chuck appeared at Brad's door. Pidge had seemed reluctant to come in with him and had dawdled outside to watch a ball game.

"So you got here all right," Brad greeted his brother. "Where's Mother?"

"Mother couldn't come," said Chuck, entering the cottage. "She's gone out to see Dad. He's being sent overseas."

"Oh," said Brad. He looked very sober.

Then he said to Chuck, "How did you get here? Did you come by yourself?"

61

"No, Gram wouldn't let me. Pidge came with me on the train."

"Pidge!" cried Brad. "I can't imagine why *he* would want to come. I'm almost positive it was Pidge who wrote the letter that's been causing me so much trouble."

Chuck blinked in surprise. "What letter?"

Brad explained briefly. Then he went on to say, "When I was making my racer, Pidge asked me to help him make one, too. He said that it was a lot of work, and he didn't know enough about building things. I told him I could only give him advice because the Derby rules didn't permit two boys to build a racer together. Pidge said no one would know the difference. When I still said I wouldn't help, he threatened to make me 'good and sorry.' That's why I think he wrote the letter."

"Let's face him with it," Chuck said angrily.

Brad shook his head. "I'm not absolutely sure he's the one. But he's the only person I can think of who might have a grudge against me."

"He did it all right. That's why I had to coax him so hard to come," said Chuck, thinking of his bicycle.

Before Brad could answer, the door opened, and Pidge came in. "Hi," said Pidge half-heartedly.

Brad looked steadily at him. "You know I made my racer all by myself, don't you, Pidge?"

Pidge's eyes slid away under Brad's intent gaze. "Yes," he muttered. "I——"

He was interrupted by a cheerful voice from the door. "Time to go for that final decision, Brad," said Mr. Black.

Brad introduced his brother and Pidge, and Mr. Black drove them all to the Derby headquarters. When they entered the room where Brad was to meet the inspectors, one of the men came forward.

"Well, Brad," he said, "you're in. After inspecting your car again thoroughly, and after seeing the expert way you handled those tools this morning, we're convinced that you built your racer yourself, unassisted. And a very good job you did, too."

"Thank you, sir," said Brad, grinning from ear to ear.

Later Chuck said to Pidge angrily, "Sending that letter was a pretty low trick. Brad told me he's sure you did it just for spite. If he hadn't passed his test so well, your letter might have kept him from racing!"

Pidge flushed. "If Brad guessed I wrote it, then why didn't he tell the inspectors? Why would he run the risk of being put out of the race?"

"He had no proof," Chuck said. "Besides, Brad isn't a tattler."

Pidge was silent, thinking of the trouble he would have been in if Brad had told. All at once Pidge realized that he himself would not have been big enough to act as Brad had done.

Feeling humbled and ashamed, Pidge said finally, "I'm awfully sorry I wrote the letter. And I'm not going to hold you to your promise about the bike."

"Well!" said Chuck in amazement. "You're turning out to be a regular fellow after all, Pidge."

By eleven o'clock the next day, Chuck and Pidge were in their seats in the stands along the course. Mr. Black had joined the other reporters and the photographers at the finish line. The Derby did not start until two, but there was so much to see that the boys did not find the waiting tedious.

Finally the races began. Brad won his first heat easily and continued to win one heat after another. When all the contestants had had their turn, Brad was one of the three winners who would now be competing for the national championship. The two others were Peter Winship of Seattle, Washington, and Steve Hall of Woodstock, Illinois.

The starter's arm flashed, and the three sleek cars swooped down the course. It was soon clear that the race would be between Brad and Peter. Chuck yelled as Brad's red car inched ahead. But Peter's silver racer soon caught up. Then Brad's car took the lead again. Inch by inch the silver racer crept up, and halfway down the hill the two were abreast, with Steve's car trailing. As they approached the finish line and the silver racer began to gain, the roar of the crowd grew deafening. Then they were across, Peter's car leading by half a length.

The roar dropped to a murmur as a voice over the loud-speaker announced that Peter Winship had won first place. Brad Evers was second.

Chuck, a lump in his throat, saw Peter and his car being lifted up on the shoulders of an admiring throng. "I wonder how Brad feels," he thought.

Just then Brad and Steve Hall were lifted above the crowd. "Brad's laughing!" Chuck cried, and felt a surge of pride in his brother.

Chuck and Pidge worked their way through the milling people to where Brad was. Photographers were taking pictures of the three top winners and their cars. The boys looked hot and dirty but very happy as they were congratulated from all sides.

"It's a shame you didn't win first prize," Chuck told Brad when he could speak to his brother.

"I was mighty lucky to get second prize," Brad laughed. "It's only a thousand dollars less than first." Then he saw Pidge and nodded cheerfully.

"I'm sorry——" Pidge began, his face reddening.

"Forget it," interrupted Brad. "How about you and Chuck having a look at the winning car?"

Pidge felt suddenly happy. "Thanks, Brad," he replied. "I'd better learn all I can about racers. I'm going to build one myself next year."

"Good idea, Pidge," said Chuck, exchanging an understanding look with Brad. "I may make one, too. One of us might even beat Brad's record."

The Captive

With the taste of a hearty breakfast still in his mouth, Clyde Mason stepped onto the back porch of the ranch house. He waved to Joe Stocks, the ranch foreman, who was standing in the doorway of the barn.

Hearing the sharp and sudden drumming of hard-hitting hoofs, the boy glanced quickly toward the "captive corral," the enclosure where the wildest horses were kept until they were broken. Now the high board fence was shaking from the impact of twelve hundred pounds of wild horse.

"Stop him, Joe!" yelled Clyde, dashing from the porch. "He'll break down the fence!" Joe had already grabbed a rope and was racing toward the corral. Opening the gate a crack, he dived inside.

Clyde squeezed into the corral in time to see the big black horse, nostrils flaring, break into a gallop. As Joe's rope snaked out through the air, the boy tensed. But he relaxed when Joe's expert throw caught the big horse around the neck and broke the force of his lunge.

Joe's heels dug hard into the ground as he was pulled after the horse. When he got his balance, he fought the big animal's power for five minutes. It was another five minutes before he could shorten the rope and snub the lunging horse close to the post in the center of the corral. Finally he made a hitch in the rope and stepped away.

The horse stood still, trembling with excitement. Clyde looked at him admiringly. He was beautiful— big without heaviness and well muscled. His coat was as black as midnight. His small ears stood up alertly, and his broad chest and sloping shoulders promised speed and strength enough to suit any rider.

Clyde stepped as close to the horse as he dared. "Did he hurt himself?" the boy asked Joe.

Joe grinned. "I can't rub him down to find out," he answered. "He looks O.K. That right foreleg seems bruised a little, but he stands well."

"He surely must have a great heart," Clyde said. "It would take courage to try to clear that fence."

Joe nodded in agreement. "And after three days without——" He stopped, stammered, and went on, "And after being alone in the corral for so long."

Clyde stared at the lanky foreman. "And after three days without *what*?" he demanded.

"Three days without food," admitted the man. "I didn't want to tell you. I know what you think of that horse, and I didn't want you to know that he's refused to eat for three days. I thought he'd get used to being penned in by now."

"Personally, I don't think he will."

These words came from behind Clyde and Joe. The boy turned and saw his father standing at the gate of the corral.

Mr. Mason's eyes reflected serious concern. "I think that horse is just too wild," he said. "And he's been free too long. I'm afraid he can't ever be tamed."

Clyde frowned. "I think he can, Dad. Haven't you always said that any horse can be broken with enough patience and gentleness?"

"Not exactly," Mr. Mason objected. "I've said that the only way to break a horse is with patience and gentleness, but I've never said that *any* horse can be broken that way. Sometimes you run into one that's just too much horse.

"Look at this one. You and Joe have had him for almost three weeks, and you still can't get near him. He's been miserable penned up, and now he won't eat. I'd let him go free."

Clyde glanced at the horse and then back at his father. "No," he replied with determination. "You may be right, but I'd like to try breaking him."

"All right, Son," Mr. Mason said, sighing. "I won't interfere any more. But if I were you, I'd do some serious thinking about that horse. I would like to see you break him, but I wouldn't want to see you kill him in the process."

"Kill him! But——" Clyde's words caught in his throat, so outraged was he at this suggestion. He opened his mouth to say more, but his father was already walking away.

70

Clyde turned to Joe. "How about it?" the boy
asked. "You don't agree with Dad, do you?"

Joe shrugged. "It's up to you, I guess."

Pivoting on his heel, Clyde went striding out of
the corral. The big horse was his, he told himself
defiantly. He was the one who had first sighted the
wild horse in a small box canyon. Day after day
he had hidden on a ledge of the canyon, watching to
be sure that the horse returned every day to this
same place. And with every passing moment his
determination to own and gentle that great proud
creature had become stronger.

At last he had managed to persuade Joe and the
other ranch hands to help him capture the horse.

The memory of the wild chase to rope the animal was still sharp in Clyde's mind. It had taken almost a whole day to catch him, get him into the ranch truck, and finally into the "captive corral."

After all that work Clyde thought that he surely had earned the right to break and ride the horse. But in spite of his keen desire to tame the spirited animal, Clyde knew that he did not have the right to ruin him.

Arguments continued to toss and turn in the disturbed boy's mind while he did his morning chores. By noon Clyde still felt that he did not want to let the horse go free, though he knew that neither his father nor Joe would approve such a decision.

This knowledge affected the boy's appetite. At lunchtime Clyde, usually famished, ate only a few bites. After the meal he said, "Dad, I'm going to take a dog and ride out to the south range. We might pick up some trace of the coyote that lamed one of our colts the other day."

"All right," said his father. He knew that Clyde only wanted an excuse to ride out alone and make up his mind definitely. "Will you be back tonight?"

"No," said Clyde. "I probably won't come back before tomorrow." He turned to Joe. "Will you keep trying to feed my horse? Maybe he'll eat a little if the feed is right there all the time." Joe nodded, and Clyde left for the main corral.

There he roped and saddled a pinto pony. Returning to the house, he packed some food and got his rifle and a blanket. Then he called to old Bob, the largest and oldest of the ranch dogs.

As Clyde rode off, he let the pinto set its own pace. The boy laughed at the way old Bob ranged wide and returned at a run, as if urging him to get on with the hunt. He relaxed in his saddle, basking in the warm sun.

After a while he rode faster, letting old Bob set the pace now. The country was getting hilly, with patches of timber. The dog's tongue soon began to loll from his mouth. Suddenly as they approached a timbered spot, Bob seemed to scent something up ahead. Clyde raised himself in the saddle, trying to get a good look at the edge of the timber.

At that instant a dim shape almost like a shadow went slinking off into the woods. Clyde kicked at the pinto's flanks excitedly. They had surprised a coyote.

Old Bob picked up the trail and slanted off into the timber, his eager barks urging Clyde on. The boy followed for a short distance and then stopped. He was waiting to see if the coyote would circle around. The dog's baying grew fainter, and Clyde started on again. He knew that he must not fall too far behind. With only old Bob after the coyote, the vicious animal might decide to turn and fight.

For almost an hour the chase continued. Clyde stopped and waited frequently, still thinking that the coyote might double back. When it did not, the lad followed along swiftly.

Clyde realized that the pursuit of the coyote was drawing him toward the canyon that contained Old Man's Mine. He was a little glad of this, for the deserted mine shaft would provide a good place to spend the night.

At last the dog's barks led Clyde directly to the abandoned silver mine. Old Bob was standing in front of the mine's black entrance. He was baying threateningly, but he was too wise to go in after his quarry.

Clyde dismounted quickly and loaded the chamber of his rifle. Calling Bob back, he ran toward the mine entrance. He paused there until he could see into the deep shadows within and then entered the mine cautiously.

He had advanced perhaps twenty-five feet when he came to an abrupt halt. He had heard a slight sound ahead of him. Light from the shaft opening revealed the ugly coyote ready to spring, its fangs bared.

Setting the rifle tight against his shoulder, Clyde fired once. The dark shape vaulted into the air, yapping. Another shot, and the coyote lay still.

As the echoes of his shots died away, the boy heard a scraping, tumbling sound. By the time he realized what it was, he could only lunge forward desperately. A great blow hit his legs and he fell, losing his breath as he struck the ground.

Slowly Clyde sat up, drawing his legs free from a pile of dirt that had caved in on him. Where the mouth of the mine had been, there was now nothing but darkness. The air was heavy with dust.

Clyde realized with panic that he was trapped in the old mine. The rotten timbers in the roof must have been ready to cave in for months, maybe years. His gunshots had been all that was needed to shift the rocks and earth above the mine and thus start in motion the slide that held him captive.

For a few moments Clyde was almost overcome with despair at his plight. Then he pulled himself together. Perhaps there was some way out after all. Rising shakily to his feet, he felt the wall of dirt with his hands. Then he began to weigh his chances of digging through it to freedom. Those chances were pretty slim, he guessed. He could not tell the extent of the cave-in. But he felt sure that the good air in this part of the mine would not hold out for many hours.

His only real chance lay with old Bob. If Bob went right home, help might arrive in time. But if the dog lingered outside—Clyde tried not to think of that possibility.

Hampered by the darkness, he began to work at the loose earth that clogged the entrance. He dug as a dog does, scooping out great handfuls of earth and tossing it behind him. Then he remembered his rifle. He turned and groped along the floor of the mine until he found it. After making sure that the safety catch was on, he gripped the gun as he would a canoe paddle. He found that he could dig much faster with the rifle butt than with his bare hands.

As Clyde worked steadily, he tried to ignore the ache that soon set into his arms and back. He put every ounce of his energy and all of his will into the digging.

The hours dragged by, and the boy's backache grew worse and worse. He had to pause often for a brief rest. When at last he had dug out part of a tunnel, he judged that four or five hours must have passed.

Now Clyde found that he had to stop oftener to rest. He was gasping for breath, and there was a strange pounding in his head. He understood the meaning of his short wind and throbbing head. The air supply was giving out.

The next time Clyde stopped, it seemed as though he could still hear his rifle digging. Perplexed, he shook his head to clear it. The scraping sounds continued. Then he knew. Someone was digging from the outside!

Clyde gathered air into his lungs to yell with all his might. But remembering the cause of the cave-in, he stifled the cry. Silently he attacked the pile of dirt again.

A short time later a hole appeared in the tunnel ahead of Clyde. Slowly and carefully Joe Stocks drew the boy through to the outside. Clyde's legs felt like rubber as he staggered weakly to his feet. The fresh night air made him dizzy, and he almost fell. But just in time his father caught him under the arms and lowered him gently to the ground.

"You just rest," he told his son. "Everything is fine now. When old Bob came home without you, we knew that something was wrong. So Joe and I got out the jeep, and Bob led us here. You just rest easy."

Clyde relaxed on the ground. As old Bob came licking at his face, he patted the dog fondly. At last he began to feel stronger. "Let's go home," he said, rising wearily.

Mr. Mason helped him into the front seat of the ranch jeep. Joe tied the pinto to the rear bumper with a long rope. Then Joe and old Bob climbed into the back seat.

When they reached the ranch, Clyde glanced at once toward the "captive corral."

"Joe," he said, "did my horse eat anything?"

Joe shook his head. "Maybe he will tomorrow."

Mr. Mason touched the boy's arm. "You can worry about the horse in the morning. Right now you need food and rest."

Clyde nodded and walked into the house. After eating the hot supper his anxious mother prepared for him, he shed his clothes and put on pajamas. Soon he was stretched out on his bed. But he did not fall asleep immediately. The darkness in the room reminded him of the darkness in the old mine. He got up and opened the window wide, breathing deeply of the cool night air.

All at once he heard the drumming of a horse's hoofs. Then a wild snort came from the "captive corral."

A firm decision formed in Clyde's mind. Quickly he pulled on a robe and his shoes. Leaving the house quietly, he ran to the corral and threw open the high board gate.

His throat was tight as he spied the dark shape on the other side of the enclosure.

"Come on, boy!" he called. "No more 'captive corral' for you. You're going home, too."

The black horse came forward, warily at first. Then he raced out of the corral, passing so close to Clyde that the boy could have touched him.

"So long," Clyde said huskily as he watched the wild horse go galloping into the night.

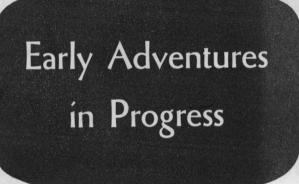

Early Adventures in Progress

Sent by Mail

"Pa, Pa!" called young Ben Taylor as he ran into the house. "There's a man down at Bixby's Inn who came all the way from New York! He's carrying mail from New York to Boston. I came past the inn just now and saw him."

"Carrying the mail all the way from New York to Boston!" Joseph Taylor cried in astonishment. "What mail can be so important that a man has to ride two hundred and fifty miles just to deliver it? And in January, too!"

"He's called a postrider, and he's going to make the trip every month," the boy continued excitedly. "He'll carry mail for people who live between the two cities, too. Governor Lovelace of New York is the one who started it."

"What strange notion will they have next?" said Mr. Taylor, shaking his head in wonder.

"After supper let's go down to the inn and see the man," suggested Ben's older brother John.

"There's work to do," Joseph Taylor reminded John sternly. "We can't rush off just to see some foolish postrider."

A moment later someone knocked at the door. It was the family's nearest neighbor, Matthew Duke.

"Joe," said Matthew, "I'm on my way to see the postrider at Bixby's Inn. I thought you might like to come with me. Mrs. Bixby told my wife that he has a letter for you."

"A letter for me!" cried Mr. Taylor, beginning to share Ben's excitement. "But how can I get it? I've no money to give the postrider right now."

"You won't need any money," Mr. Duke told him. "The postal charge is paid before the mail starts. The one who sends it pays for it."

"What happens if the mail doesn't get delivered?" Mr. Taylor asked, puzzled. "Then the sender has just wasted his money."

"The mail will get through all right," replied Mr. Duke. "This country isn't wild any more. This is 1673. We haven't even had trouble with the Indians here in Connecticut for a couple of years."

"Well, I'll go with you," Mr. Taylor decided at last. "John, you might as well come, too."

At Bixby's Inn the occupants of the big public room were all discussing the new postal service. The postrider sat talking with Mr. Bixby.

"Well, Joe Taylor," said Mr. Bixby, "you have a letter from your wife's brother, William Collins, in New York. He wants you to send your son John down to live with him. His only son died, and he needs someone to help him in his business. He'll even pay John's way to New York."

"It seems strange that you should know what's in *my* letter," said Mr. Taylor. "Wasn't it sealed?"

The innkeeper flushed; then he chuckled. "Well, I confess I'm a curious man. Since the sealing wax had come off and the letter was open, I just couldn't help reading it. Here it is. See if every word I told you isn't exactly as the letter says."

Smiling, Mr. Taylor read the letter to himself.

"You're right, Mr. Bixby," said Joseph Taylor when he finished reading the letter. "William owns several ships and needs a boy to learn the shipping business. But New York is ninety miles away. I don't think that we would want our boy to go so far from home. And how would he get there if we did decide to send him?"

At this point the postrider spoke up. "The boy could go with me on my return trip. I'm supposed to take travelers along if they wish to accompany me. Of course Mr. Collins would have to pay for my keep on the way, as well as the boy's."

"Well, I'll think about it," replied Mr. Taylor.

"I'll be coming back from Boston in about three weeks," the postrider went on. "If you decide to send the boy with me, have him ready with a good horse to ride. I'll bring the horse back to you on my next trip to Meriden."

For the next few days the Taylor family talked of nothing but Mr. Collins' letter. Mrs. Taylor's family had come from England. When they arrived in New York, all but her oldest brother had gone on to settle in Connecticut. He had stayed in New York and become a wealthy shipowner. Until the arrival of the letter, Mrs. Taylor's only news of her brother had come from occasional travelers passing through Meriden. She had sent word to him in the same way.

85

To John, the idea of going to New York seemed thrilling at first. But the more he thought about it, the more reluctant the boy was to leave his family. He hoped his parents would decide not to send him.

One day, however, John heard his mother say to his father, "It may be a good idea for John to go. We have four strong, healthy sons, Joseph, and my brother has none."

"I've been hoping you would say that," replied Mr. Taylor. "Ben is old enough now to help me in the fields. Jonas and Abraham will be able to help before long, too. I hate to see John go so far away, but we must consider his future."

"What do you think, John?" asked his mother.

A lump rose in John's throat, but he answered bravely, "If you think it best for me to go, I'll do as you wish."

For the next two weeks Mrs. Taylor was busy getting John's few clothes in order. The whole family made a fuss over him, and he enjoyed himself in spite of his sadness at leaving.

The postrider journeyed to Boston and back in a little over three weeks. When he arrived again at Meriden, John's clothes were already rolled up, ready to be strapped to the saddle. His horse had been groomed for the trip. And John himself was as ready as he would ever be to leave his home and family.

The next morning John rose at daybreak. As he dressed, he shivered with the cold and with dread of the unknown life before him. His mother's good breakfast seemed tasteless, but he ate it to put off as long as possible the moment of parting. Finally John mounted his horse, after bidding a sorrowful farewell to his family gathered at the door.

"Good-by, Son, good-by," called his mother. Her eyes, brimming with tears, followed her son until he was out of sight.

At the inn John joined the postrider, and off they jogged, their horses abreast. The farms of Meriden were soon behind them. John wondered drearily if he would ever see Meriden again.

Once past the farms, the two riders entered the woods and followed an old Indian trail. Most of the trip, John knew, would be through the woods.

On and on the two rode. The trail, buried under the February snow, was so faint that John knew he could never have found it by himself. But the postrider seemed to be familiar with it.

By midafternoon John was tired and cold. He had been in the saddle since daybreak except for a half-hour stop for lunch.

Thinking of what lay ahead in New York, John asked the postrider, "Do you know my uncle?"

"I have seen him," the man replied, "but I don't know him. I've heard that he's a good and honest gentleman."

John derived some comfort from the words, but not much. He rode on in silence, wondering what New York and his uncle would be like.

When night fell, John asked, "Are we going on in the dark?"

"It isn't much farther to the house where we're to lodge tonight," answered his guide. "I have a parcel to deliver to the family there."

The trail began to widen a bit, and the postrider stopped. "I think we're nearing the house now," he said. "But we'll have to cross a river before we can reach it. You stay with the horses. I'll walk ahead to see what condition the river is in. It should be frozen solid enough for us to cross on the ice, though the steep banks on either side may be slippery."

Uneasily John watched his companion leave while he waited in the dark forest with the horses. All around him in the gloom were weird shadows. A sudden rustle in the bushes behind him made him start, and the horses moved restlessly. What was that? Could it be a bear?

Just then there came a shout from the postrider up ahead. "Come on now, boy."

With a nervous glance over his shoulder at the still rustling bushes, John rode as fast as he could in the direction of the shout. To his great relief he was soon able to distinguish the dim form of his companion.

"The riverbank is just a little farther on," said the man as he remounted his horse. "Follow me."

Presently the two horses with their riders were plunging down a steep, slippery bank. The boy's heart was in his mouth. He expected his horse to stumble and fall at any minute. Then, happily, he found himself on level ground at the river's edge. Now he could see quite clearly. The moonlight, which had not penetrated the forest, shone brightly on the ice-covered river.

"Slowly, boy," cautioned the postrider. "The ice is none too firm. We'd better take it carefully."

It seemed a miracle to John that they were able to make their way across the thin ice and up the steep bank on the other side without an accident.

Just beyond the river, near a fork
in the trail, the postrider pulled up at
a house. He knocked on the door.
"Postrider from Boston with something for you," he called.

The door opened and a man stepped out. When
he recognized the postrider, he exclaimed heartily,
"Come in! Did you deliver my letter in Boston?"

"I did," said the postrider. "Now I'm bringing
a reply, and a parcel from your relatives there."

"This regular mail service does beat all!" the
farmer exclaimed. "Governor Lovelace surely had
a good idea when he started it. Now come in and
spend the night." Then the farmer noticed John.
"You, too, young fellow. I'll tend to your horses
while you both have some supper."

John nodded wearily. "Thank you, sir. It will feel good to get inside."

Satisfied that their horses would be well taken care of, John and the postrider gratefully ate the hot food set out by the farmer's wife. Then they threw themselves down on a feather bed spread for them on the floor, and fell asleep at once.

The next morning, after an early breakfast, the two travelers were off again. That night's stopping place was an inn. There the postrider left mail for the people in that vicinity.

For three more days John and his guide followed the narrow roads and trails, stopping only at places where the postrider had to pick up or deliver mail. Several times the boy saw bear or wildcat tracks on the road and was thankful that he had company. They crossed many streams, either on ice or at shallow fords. Each night was spent at an inn or at a house along the way.

At the end of the fifth day, the postrider said, "I think we shall reach New York tomorrow."

For the last few days John had been trying not to think about the end of the journey. Now, at the postrider's words, his fears returned. Would his uncle like him? Would John himself like the shipping business? Would his work please his uncle? Would he ever see his family again? A new wave of homesickness swept over him.

At noon the next day the two riders approached the Harlem River. John could see that there was no solid ice over it and no bridge on which they could cross. The water was too deep to ford.

"How will we get across?" he asked.

"We'll ferry over," said his guide. And as they neared the river, John saw a raft with a man on it pulled up at the shore.

"Why, you're the postrider!" cried the ferryman in surprise as the two stopped at the raft. "Have you been to Boston and back already?"

"Indeed I have," the postrider replied proudly.

The ferryman soon poled his passengers to the opposite shore. Then, through the town of Harlem, over the Manhattan hills, and finally into the town of New York they rode.

The postrider went at once to his headquarters in a coffee shop. John dismounted and followed his companion into the crowded room. All the men in the place swarmed around the postrider and patted him on the back. "Wait until the governor hears this!" said one man. "His first postrider has been to Boston and back. It's certainly a great day for the colonies of New York and Massachusetts!"

In a moment the postrider turned and beckoned to John. "This is William Collins' nephew from Meriden, Connecticut," he told the men. "We must send someone for his uncle."

This was done, and before very long a man and a woman came into the shop. Since John was the only boy there, they spied him quickly.

"John, my boy!" cried the man in a jolly voice. "Come and greet your Uncle William and your Aunt Sarah. We're glad to have you here."

John walked forward and shook hands shyly.

"I do hope you'll be happy with us," said Mrs. Collins, smiling. "We shall try not to let you get lonely or homesick."

"After all, John," said his uncle, "with this new postal service, you can send a letter home and get a reply in a month or six weeks. Why, it will be almost like having your family right next door!"

Suddenly John's dread of his new life vanished, and he smiled for the first time. "I'd like you to meet the postrider who brought me here," he said. "I guess I'm the biggest package he had to deliver on his whole trip to Boston and back."

News for the Gazette

Timothy Waring was an apprentice to the editor of the *Fielding Gazette*. Timothy's contract said that he must work in Mr. Fielding's print shop until his eighteenth birthday. Though that was six long years away, Timothy did not mind. He was proud to have a part in printing one of the few newspapers published in the American colonies in 1776.

More than anything in the world Timothy wanted to become the editor of a newspaper, as his hero, Benjamin Franklin, had been. Nowhere else could he learn his trade better than in the place he was now. Already he could set type and run the printing presses, and he was looking forward to the day when he would have enough experience to gather news and write it up for the paper.

One afternoon in early July, Mr. Fielding turned from the case where he was setting type and looked in astonishment at his young helper.

"What, Timmy?" he said. "You want a day off during the week? A fine apprentice you are!"

"Oh, no, sir, not a whole day off," said Timothy, twisting his apron nervously. "I wouldn't have to leave until five, after the paper has gone to press. I can walk home in three hours. Then in the morning I'll get up before daylight and be back here in plenty of time to deliver the papers. You see, sir, now that my brother Andy is away at the war, I'm the eldest. And it's Mother's birthday—and I have always helped her celebrate it before——"

Mr. Fielding nodded slowly, his eyes twinkling, as he looked down at the boy's eager face.

"Well, yes, I'll let you off, but don't be asking favors like this too often. If you'll take good care of my mare, Nellie, you may ride her. But see to it that you are back promptly at seven tomorrow morning."

Mr. Fielding reached into his pocket and laid a coin in Timothy's hand. "You deserve it. You've been a good lad. And now run along, because I'm holding the press until midnight. A postrider may bring news from the convention in Philadelphia.

I have a feeling in my bones that the Declaration of Independence has been signed. I've left a space vacant on the front page for the story, and I'll hold the space until midnight. It will be the best news that folks have heard in all their lives."

Timothy stopped short in the act of taking off his apron. "Then you think a postrider might still come to town with the news tonight?"

"That I do," replied Mr. Fielding firmly.

A short time later Timothy was heading for home. In spite of the dust and the heat, Nellie, the mare, loped steadily along the yellow ribbon of road. But Timothy had forgotten for the moment that he was homeward bound. He had even forgotten the new pair of scissors he was bringing as a birthday gift for his mother.

He was thinking of the same thing that most people in the thirteen colonies were thinking of at that time. Each colony had sent delegates to a convention in Philadelphia to consider an important paper called the Declaration of Independence. If all the delegates signed the Declaration, it would mean that the people of the colonies wished to be declared free and independent of England.

Some people thought that the delegates would not dare to sign the paper. If they did, they would be considered guilty of treason. And if the American Revolution failed, what would be their punishment?

"It takes brave men, Nellie, to run a risk like that," said Timothy. "Oh, I hope a postrider comes tonight in time for Mr. Fielding to print the story in tomorrow's paper."

All week long the town had waited anxiously for word from Philadelphia. Throughout the colonies it was known that as soon as a decision had been reached by the delegates in Philadelphia, reliable messengers would be sent out in every direction. But no messenger had appeared, and the suspense was growing harder and harder to bear.

On Timothy's arrival home, he forgot the plight of the colonies in the warmth of his mother's greeting. She had not expected him so early, and she was delighted with the scissors he had brought.

Tom, his younger brother, helped him rub down the mare while Jip, the puppy, barked joyfully at his heels, and his sister Jenny asked him endless questions about his work. As soon as they could, the boys ran to the creek for a swim before supper.

The creek was across the oatfield but still within hearing distance of the supper bell. After a half-hour of cool splashing, the two boys heard the bell. They dressed hurriedly and picked their way over the new oats back to the house.

"I declare!" said Timothy sheepishly as he came into the kitchen. "I left my shoes and socks down by the creek. And my only pair of shoes at that!"

Tom and Jenny laughed gleefully. Tim's forget-
fulness of shoes and socks seemed to prove that
he was still a country boy at heart. Until now they
had been feeling a little in awe of his new dignity
as apprentice to a publisher.

"Eat your supper while it's hot, Timmy," said his
mother. "You can fetch your shoes afterwards."

It was a merry meal, with chicken, hot biscuits,
and a birthday cake that Jenny had baked. Tim's
tongue was loosened, and Mr. Fielding would never
have recognized the boy for his quiet apprentice.

"My apprenticeship will be up when I'm eighteen.
Then I'm going to be an editor and have my own
newspaper," boasted the lad.

"An editor at eighteen?" scoffed Jenny.

"Benjamin Franklin wasn't much older than that when he became an editor," Timothy said. "And Mr. Fielding says I'll make a good newspaperman. He's teaching me everything about a newspaper. I wish I could do something for him."

After supper the family sat on the doorstep, talking about the Declaration of Independence and the hopes that beat high in the heart of every patriot. Only when they were going to bed did Timothy remember his shoes. He must get them. They were the only real shoes he had ever owned.

"Tom, you go with Timmy," said Mrs. Waring. "But I don't want you boys trampling the oats in the dark. You'd better go around by the road and take a lantern with you."

The boys did as their mother suggested. Holding the lantern low to light their path, they followed a ditch running along one side of the road. As they neared the footbridge that would take them across the ditch to a lane leading to the creek, the quiet was broken by a loud groan.

"What's that?" asked Timothy nervously, raising his lantern high. The light revealed nothing, but soon another sound came from the direction of the ditch—a few mumbled phrases that the boys could not understand. Tom slipped a trembling hand into his brother's. They stepped forward cautiously, and now they could see a horse that had fallen into the ditch. Its rider was caught painfully beneath the animal, whose neck appeared to be broken.

Tom hurried home for his mother and sister, and the four of them managed to drag the injured man out from under his horse. Somehow they carried him to the house, where he soon revived.

"My horse was killed by the fall," he cried, "but I must get to the *Fielding Gazette* office! I am a postrider from Philadelphia with important news!" He tried to rise but fell back on the pillows.

"Tell me the news," begged Timothy. "I'll ride with it at once to the editor of the *Gazette*." And he scarcely breathed while the man told his story.

Thus it happened that Timothy and Nellie made the journey back to town that dark night. It was not the ride that every boy dreams of taking some- time—a wild gallop for freedom or a swift, thrilling dash to a rescue. It was a slow, patient jog along an unseen, rut-filled road, with the uncanny cries of screech owls sounding through the darkness.

Timothy had an urge to give Nellie a kick, but he remembered the fate of the postrider's horse. He proceeded slowly and cautiously, a far braver deed than riding at breakneck speed.

Later an amazed Mr. Fielding saw a barefoot boy burst into his office.

"It's signed!" cried Timothy. "The Declaration of Independence has been signed!"

Without a word Mr. Fielding walked to the type case and commenced setting up the story as the boy told it to him. The next morning, readers of the *Gazette* rejoiced at the great news.

To Timothy's surprise there was an item in the paper about his part in bringing the news. The item said, moreover, that his master, to show his trust in Timothy, intended to make the boy his heir, and that he would become a partner in the *Gazette*.

"Oh, Mr. Fielding, thank you!" The boy flushed and wriggled his toes with embarrassment.

Mr. Fielding's eyes, twinkling as usual, traveled downward to Timothy's bare feet. "Come, son," the editor said. "Let's go down to the shoemaker. I think my new partner needs a pair of shoes."

All Aboard!

On the hot summer morning of August 9, 1831,
a great crowd was pressing through the Albany
streets to see one of America's newest miracles.
Derek Dexter was among that eager throng. He
ducked and squeezed and pushed until at last he
saw it—the iron horse.

There it was, the demon machine, panting and
puffing on the track. It was the *DeWitt Clinton*.
That day the engine would haul its load the whole
seventeen miles from Albany to Schenectady, and
what was more, all the way back.

The *DeWitt Clinton* had enormous wheels and a
smokestack rearing loftily above the steam boiler.
An important-looking man stood on a tiny platform

behind the locomotive. His job was to operate the
engine and steer the train.

A car behind the engineer held a pile of wood
and two water barrels draped with a leather hose.
Then came three vehicles resembling stagecoaches.
They were linked to the fuel car and to each other
by chains. Each coach could hold eight or nine
passengers and had some additional seats on top.
Attached to the final coach were flatcars. These
were intended for freight or baggage, but today
they held wooden benches for the guests invited to
take the grand tour to Schenectady.

Derek noticed all details of the train and imagined
the delight of riding on it. Strolling alongside it,
he stepped on the toes of someone's polished boots.

"Excuse me, sir," Derek apologized to the owner of the shiny boots, who was a well-dressed, bare-headed gentleman. In the crook of his left arm he balanced his big beaver hat. He was sketching on a paper spread over the hat crown.

"What are you drawing, sir?" Derek asked.

The artist plied his pencil in silence for a few minutes. Then he said, "You realize, perhaps, that this August 9, 1831, is a historic occasion?"

"Because of the train?" asked Derek.

"Precisely. The first official trip of the *DeWitt Clinton* will be written into the history of America— and with it the name of William Brown."

"Are you William Brown?"

"At your service," said the man. "And you?"

"Derek Dexter. I'm twelve. I live in Albany with my grandparents."

"You're a passenger for Schenectady?"

Derek grinned. "Oh, no. I'd love to go, but I can't. Tell me, sir, are you going?"

"I wouldn't miss it for the world!"

Mr. Brown thrust the paper into the pocket of his satin waistcoat. Then pointing out a flatcar, he said, "Yonder is my bench. You have my per-mission to sit there for a moment—just for fun."

An excellent suggestion! Derek soon was perched on the flatcar. About him bobbed the passengers going on that historic trip, dignified gentlemen with long whiskers and high hats; ladies in wide-skirted dresses with sunshades and bonnets.

The captain of the train was busily collecting the fares. He talked with Mr. Brown, who gestured toward Derek. Then the captain scrambled back to his seat at the rear of the fuel car.

A blast from the captain's tin whistle drowned out all conversation. Sudden tension gripped both travelers and spectators. Derek leaped to his feet. "I must get off!" he cried.

The whistle shrilled again. The engine wheezed and grunted and after a terrific lurch began rolling. As the slack in the chains was taken up, the coaches rolled, too, and then the flatcars—slowly, one car at a time.

The result was wild confusion. Coaches and cars collided and banged; every passenger was dislodged and thrown into the lap of the person behind him. Men roared astonished protests; women shrieked in horror. The engineer tottered and clung to his throttle. The captain, clutching an iron bar of the fuel car, hung suspended like a monkey.

But the train was moving forward. Derek, after picking himself up from the tangle of people and overturned benches, tugged at Mr. Brown's wrist.

"I must get off. I told Grandmother——"

Before the words were fairly out of his mouth, a new excitement threatened. Showers of sparks

burst from the giant smokestack of the engine. The
wind was carrying the sparks in a fiery flood that
dropped on the ladies' fluffy clothing and the silky,
flowing whiskers of the men. Cotton cloth flared
into jets of crimson. Wool smoldered. A beautiful
velvet bonnet burst into flames and was snatched
from the head of its terrified wearer.

Everyone was in a panic, smothering the flames.

Derek pounded Mr. Brown's blazing shirt collar.
Mr. Brown vigorously pounded Derek. Everyone
around them slapped someone else, rescuing a friend
from disaster.

But the train went on. The engineer resolutely
sent his iron steed over the rails. The shower of
sparks did not cease, but it diminished.

All the passengers were badly singed, and their garments torn and blackened. In spite of this, they laughed. They had expected an adventure, and they could become accustomed to the dodging that was necessary to prevent any serious damage.

Only Derek was subdued and sober. With every minute he was farther from Albany. Grandmother would be searching for him, worried and perhaps angry. What could he do? He peered anxiously up the ribbon of track.

A water tank was coming into view. Mr. Brown said that they would stop to take on water.

The engineer, doubtful of his brakes, applied them powerfully. What happened then was exactly like the starting performance, but in reverse.

The engine balked and was banged by the fuel car. The fuel car was bumped by the coaches, and the coaches were jolted by the trailing flatcars. Then the whole train shuddered convulsively and stopped.

"Something must be wedged in between the cars to avoid the perils of starting and stopping," Mr. Brown declared. "Fence rails would do. Who'll volunteer to help tear down that fence over there?"

Derek volunteered along with the men, and with Mr. Brown leading, they all tumbled out and set to work. When the rails were in place, the captain tooted his whistle, and the travelers all scrambled aboard again.

Easily, without jarring a bit, the train was off.

"The worst is past," Mr. Brown said to Derek. "Isn't this comfortable?"

"I ought to be at home," grumbled Derek.

"You ought," agreed the artist, smiling. "But what can't be cured must be endured. So why not be happy? I'll guarantee that fifty years from today you'll have no regrets."

Derek considered the advice. He couldn't be *quite* happy. And yet the riding was lots of fun!

After that pause at the water tank, the *DeWitt Clinton* chugged along triumphantly through the open fields. Astonished cattle eyed it distrustfully, frightened colts squealed, dogs barked, and farmers leaned on their plows to stare in amazement.

With all the delay, it took an hour and forty-five minutes to reach Schenectady, where more than a thousand citizens were assembled to welcome the train. During the two-hour wait at that city, there were enthusiastic speeches and refreshments.

The return trip was calm and took just thirty-eight minutes. The passengers said that the railroad was proving its worth and would speed the progress of the nation. They joked and sang.

As the engine braked to a stop, Derek was silent.

"Do you want me to go to your grandmother and explain your absence?" asked Mr. Brown.

"No, thank you." Derek could not let the artist share his scolding. "Good-by, sir." Derek raced down the street toward his home.

"Well!" Grandmother said, looking up as Derek stepped in the door. "So you went on a journey?"

"I—I didn't mean to, ma'am. But I did enjoy it."

"Didn't mean to? Why, you let that artist pay your fare. Deacon Pierce was on the platform and heard him talking to the train captain about you."

Derek gulped. That idea hadn't occurred to him.

"Grandfather is at the hotel now," Grandmother added, "to repay that artist fellow. We Dexters don't accept such favors. We pay our own way. Your supper's on the table. I saved it for you."

Derek dawdled over the milk and gingerbread. He had eaten heartily at Schenectady.

Then Grandfather came in. He was bluff and snowy-bearded. "I've just talked to Mr. Brown. He says you didn't intend to take that trip, Derek. You didn't suspect the trick he played on you."

"No, sir, I didn't."

"Brown says he thought it was a fine experience for a lad of twelve. And I guess he's right. A tale for you to tell your children—that you rode on the first train running between the cities of Albany and Schenectady."

Grandfather took something from his vest pocket. "You know what that artist's done? He's made a sketch of the train and cut a silhouette of it out of black paper. He plans to exhibit the silhouette, and here's the sketch for Derek."

"My lands!" exclaimed Grandmother.

Derek took the paper. Yes, there was the *DeWitt Clinton*, so lifelike that he could almost smell the smoke and hear the captain's tin whistle. Below the picture Mr. Brown had written *All Aboard!*

Derek glanced at his grandparents. "Would you like me to describe the ride?" he asked timidly.

"Do," replied Grandfather, "for next time *I'm* going."

"It was splendid," Derek began. "We went awfully fast. We went almost thirty miles an hour!"

Farewell to the Boneshaker

As eleven-year-old Johnny King started out the back door, his mother called, "Johnny, where are you going? We'll be leaving for the Exposition in about an hour, you know."

"I'm just going for a bicycle ride, Mother," he called back. "I'm all dressed for the Exposition, and I'll be back in plenty of time. I can't wait to see the big Corliss steam engine that runs all the machinery at the Exposition."

"All you think about are machines and that boneshaker of yours!" exclaimed his sister Lucy.

But Johnny did not hear her. He was already mounting his beloved bicycle, a two-wheeled vehicle made of wood. Down the street he went, bouncing up and down on the wooden saddle as the wooden wheels jolted over the cobblestone street. The contraption was indeed a boneshaker.

An hour later Johnny's family was ready to go to the Centennial Exposition. Like everyone else in Philadelphia in 1876, the Kings found it exciting to have such a large affair right in their own city. Now that they were actually going to see it, they were anxious to get started. But Johnny was not home yet.

Fifteen minutes passed. Then half an hour went by. Still Johnny had not come home. The family became more and more impatient.

Finally the doorbell rang, and Mr. King hurried to answer it. There was a policeman, with Johnny in his arms. The boy's face was pale and bruised. His body was limp, except for one hand. In that hand he clutched a handle bar of the boneshaker.

"He was going too fast when he hit a stretch of rough road," the policeman explained. "I'm afraid his boneshaker is completely destroyed."

"Oh," wept Mrs. King as the policeman carried the boy inside. "I knew this would happen. There will never be another boneshaker in this family!"

Although to everyone's relief Johnny had only some bruises and a bump on his head, his mother thought that the trip to the Centennial Exposition should be postponed. The next day Johnny was up and about again, but his boneshaker was gone forever. There was not even enough of it left to use for firewood.

The King family decided to go to the Exposition on the following Saturday. Johnny was more eager than before to see the Corliss engine. Ever since he had lost his precious boneshaker, thoughts of the gigantic engine filled his mind constantly.

When Saturday came, Mr. King kept his eye on Johnny until everyone was ready. Then he called a carriage, and the family was driven to a gateway through which hundreds of people were entering a vast enclosure. Inside were scores of buildings among trees, lawns, fountains, and flower beds.

"There must be a million people!" cried Lucy as the Kings got out of the carriage.

Once inside the gate, they gazed with interest at the many buildings. Johnny's eyes darted from side to side seeking Machinery Hall, where the Corliss engine was. He knew how its great driving rods must rise and fall, but he just had to see them in action for himself.

"It would take months to see all of this!" cried Mrs. King. "Where in the world shall we begin?"

"I suggest we look into the Main Building first," said Mr. King.

"I'm going straight to Machinery Hall," Johnny announced firmly.

"You'll get lost!" wailed his mother.

"He has a tongue in his head," said Mr. King. "And he knows what he wants to see. You and

Lucy probably won't care to go to Machinery Hall, so Johnny might as well see it now. He can stay there until I come for him."

Mr. King went with Johnny to the outer door of the big building. "I shall be back in three hours," he said. "There will be a clock inside somewhere. Look at it once in a while."

Johnny smiled and nodded. From within the hall came a mingling of wonderful noises. He heard innumerable clanging, grinding, and whining sounds, all of them made by machines!

The boy's heart thumped as he entered the inner door. Towering in the distance was the massive engine. Johnny tried to hurry toward it, but the aisles were blocked by great crowds of people.

His progress was slow. Too slow! Sometimes he was forced to stop and look at the exhibits he was passing. He saw all kinds of machines being demonstrated—sewing machines, weaving machines, power saws, and many others. There were models of sailing vessels, steamships, and warships. But Johnny was not really interested in them. What he wanted to see was the big Corliss engine.

He felt like shouting, "Hurry up; go on!" to the tall men and women in front of him. Instead, he began worming his way between them. But now the crowd was growing even thicker, and the boy had to stop again.

Wearily he turned his head to see what kind of exhibit was beside him. Then his heart seemed to stop beating. He leaned against a pole of the iron fence that separated the exhibits from the visitors. He held onto it firmly so that he could not be torn away from that spot.

"Move on, there, sonny!" ordered a voice from the crowd.

Johnny continued to gaze at the wonderful exhibit. "I'll never move on," he replied firmly.

"Don't mind if people yell at you," said someone beside Johnny. He looked up into the friendly eyes of a large red-headed man who was guarding the exhibit. "Want to come inside?" asked the man.

Johnny gave him a warm look of gratitude, and the guard opened a gate in the iron fence. Johnny hurried in and sat down on a chair.

"Are you particularly interested in this exhibit?" asked the guard.

"Yes," said Johnny. "I might say that I am."

"Then stay a while," the man invited.

"I will," Johnny replied, staring as if in a trance at the object on a platform beside him.

Three hours after Johnny had entered Machinery Hall, Mr. King returned to look for his son. Mrs. King and Lucy had already gone home exhausted. Mr. King felt sure that the boy would be ready to leave by this time.

When Mr. King did not find Johnny waiting at the entrance, he looked about for the Corliss engine and hastened toward it. That was where Johnny would be, he thought. He searched the entire area around the big engine with its pounding pistons, but Johnny was not to be seen.

His father felt a little helpless when he realized how many places Johnny might be. He stood still for a moment, looking around the hall. Suddenly he saw the boy a few feet away. Johnny was sitting inside a railing at one of the exhibits, talking to the red-headed man in charge. On a nearby table lay drawings that explained the exhibit to anyone who cared to study them.

As Mr. King walked toward his son, he saw a strange vehicle labeled "Gentleman's Hobby Horse." It consisted of two wheels joined by a horizontal wooden bar with a wooden saddle on it. Another such vehicle, whose wheels were connected by a curved bar, was labeled "Lady's Hobby Horse." Neither had pedals. The rider had to propel one of these machines, apparently, by pushing his feet on the ground.

A third vehicle with pedals and a stronger frame was familiar to Mr. King. He had seen one just like it unpacked at his home. Later he had seen the splintered remains. This third vehicle was labeled "The Bicycle or Boneshaker."

As Mr. King stood gazing at the exhibit, Johnny turned and saw him. "Come in, Father!" cried the boy, pulling Mr. King through the little gate in the iron railing and pointing. "There's what I want. And it's not a boneshaker. I'm sure that Mother won't mind my having this."

Mr. King raised his eyes to the platform at the back of the exhibit stall. There stood still another two-wheeled machine.

"Look, Father," said Johnny, his voice trembling. "This bicycle has steel rims and wire spokes and rubber tires! It's called Humber's Spider."

Mr. King looked and groaned. The front wheel of Humber's Spider was about three times as high as the rear wheel—it must have been at least sixty inches in height! The rider was expected to perch on a small saddle above this huge front wheel and propel himself with pedals.

"That's what I want!" Johnny cried again.

Mr. King examined Humber's Spider in dismay. His eyes measured the distance from the saddle of the machine to the pedal at its lowest point. Then he noted the length of Johnny's legs.

"Not yet, Johnny," sighed Mr. King in relief.

"When I'm tall enough, Father? Promise you'll get me one when I'm tall enough," Johnny insisted.

Mr. King addressed the guard. "Do you think there's a chance of the front wheel shrinking and the back wheel getting larger?" he asked.

"You can't tell, sir. It might be."

"Well, if that ever happens, I promise to get you one, Johnny," Mr. King said. "Now let's look at the big engine. I don't suppose you got that far."

Johnny walked with his father toward the Corliss engine, but his thoughts were now centered on the Spider. Johnny had even forgotten his boneshaker. He knew that coachmen sometimes spoke of an especially fine horse as "sweet." That was a good word to describe Humber's Spider, he thought. It was sweet.

Newfangled Notions

"Dear me, Nan Marshall," said Mrs. Dana, who was in charge of the needlework booth. "You don't mean to say you've come to the fair without your quilt?"

Nan nodded, winking back the tears that rose in her blue eyes. All summer long she had worked piecing the quilt. She had sewed thousands of tiny, even stitches so that she would have a handsome quilt to exhibit at the County Fair. Then in the excitement of departure, she had left it at home.

"We could get it here by one o'clock," suggested Nan's mother. "My son Jimmie took our horse and buggy back to town, but he's coming to the fair again this afternoon. He could bring it."

"A rule's a rule," said Mrs. Dana. "The quilt must be here by half-past ten."

Adapted and reprinted by permission of the publisher, J. B. Lippincott Company, from *Father's Big Improvements* by Caroline D. Emerson. Copyright, 1936, by J. B. Lippincott Company.

"If I could only get word to Jimmie!" said Mrs. Marshall hopelessly.

Suddenly an alert expression came over her friend's face. "That newfangled machine might be of some use," cried Mrs. Dana. "Come with me."

As Nan and her mother hurried after Mrs. Dana, they were too excited to notice the dark clouds that were beginning to fill the sky. They followed their friend to a small building beside the grandstand.

"There's one of those newfangled affairs in here that you talk over," explained Mrs. Dana. "They have run a wire to the Town Hall to show people what the thing can do. My husband has been here fussing with it for a week. I could hardly get him home for meals."

"My husband's been talking about it, too," said Mrs. Marshall. "It's called a telephone."

"Sometimes it works, and sometimes it doesn't," said Mrs. Dana. "But if it gets that quilt here in time, it'll be worth all the fuss that's made over it."

Inside they saw Mr. Dana standing by a queer box on the wall. Two black tubes

were fastened to the box with long cords. There was a bell and a handle to ring it by.

"We want to catch Jimmie Marshall as he drives past the Town Hall," panted Mrs. Dana, quite out of breath. "He left here about twenty minutes ago, and he'll just be getting there. Tell him to drive home, get his sister's quilt, and hurry back to the fair immediately."

Mr. Dana was becoming confused by all this talk. "I'll try," he said. He rang the little bell on the box. Nan watched eagerly as Mr. Dana picked up the black tubes and held one of them to his ear. He spoke right into the other black tube.

"HELLO!" shouted Mr. Dana so loudly that Nan jumped. One could almost have heard him at the Town Hall, without any wire between, she thought.

"HELLO!" shouted Mr. Dana once more. Then he hung up the tube and rang the bell again.

"The man at the other end has probably gone home," said Mrs. Dana.

At last Mr. Dana managed to get the box to say something to him, but Nan could not hear what it was. Then Mr. Dana began speaking in very clear tones. "Send someone out to get Jimmie Marshall as he drives past. Send someone to catch Jimmie Marshall—— Oh, all right, I'll wait."

Nan stood first on one foot and then on the other. It seemed as if that telephone were going to keep them waiting forever. She doubted if it had really said anything to a man away back in town anyway. It seemed impossible.

"Sounds as though we're going to have a storm," said Mr. Dana as they all stood and waited. The rumbling of thunder seemed very near.

All at once Mr. Dana stood erect and held the black tube close to his ear. "HELLO!" he shouted. "Oh, hello, is that Jimmie Marshall?"

Nan's eyes began to gleam. Had the thing really worked? Could they talk with Jimmie when they were on the fairground and he was in the Town Hall? She crept close to Mr. Dana—yes, that really was Jimmie's voice, only very faint and far away.

"Oh!" gasped Nan with breathless delight.

"Tell him to come back here as fast as he can," cried Mrs. Marshall excitedly, "and to bring——"

"One thing at a time, now, one thing at a time," implored Mr. Dana. Then he shouted to Jimmie, "Your mother says to come back as fast as you can. Do you hear? Come back as fast as you can."

"He must be back here by half-past ten," cried Mrs. Marshall.

"Be back by half-past ten," roared Mr. Dana.

"And bring Nan's quilt," cried Mrs. Marshall.

"What's that?" asked Mr. Dana.

"Quilt. Q-u-i-l-t," repeated Mrs. Marshall. "Tell him to go home and get his sister's quilt."

Mr. Dana turned back to the telephone. "Go
home and get your s——"

But just then there came a flash of lightning and
then a crash. Mr. Dana dropped the black tubes
that he held and jumped halfway across the floor.
Nan hid her face in her mother's violet silk skirt.
The crash of thunder was followed by a downpour
of rain. There were cries from outside as everyone on the fairground dashed for shelter.

When Mr. Dana gingerly took up the black tube
again, not a single word could he get from it. He
rang the bell and he shouted until he was hoarse,

but no answer came. There was nothing to do but settle down beside the useless telephone and wait till the storm was over. Nan looked ruefully at the box on the wall. It was worse than useless, getting up one's hopes all for nothing!

Mrs. Marshall tried to talk courteously to Mr. and Mrs. Dana. She did not like the storm, and she was worried about Jimmie and disappointed about the quilt. Jimmie was probably driving posthaste to the fairground through all this storm and without the quilt! These modern inventions tried her patience. Her husband was all for them. But she knew that they were not to be depended upon.

"In a few years there'll be a telephone in every house," Mr. Dana was saying. "It is one of the most remarkable inventions of the century."

Mrs. Marshall was quite sure there wasn't going to be one in *her* house, not if she could prevent it! There was another crash of thunder, and she put her arm tightly around Nan. If she had her way, someone would invent a machine to do away with thundershowers!

Above the thunder and rain came the sound of the clock on the grandstand. It struck ten, and Nan counted each stroke with a sinking heart. Her quilt must be at the fairground by half-past ten, but there seemed no way short of magic to get it there if Jimmie didn't bring it.

Meanwhile, Jimmie had been having excitement also. On leaving the fairground, he had driven quickly back to town and on down the main street. The town looked very empty. Stores were closed, and most of the people were out at the fairground.

As Jimmie neared the Town Hall, he saw a man dash out to the sidewalk and stand waving his arm wildly.

"Whoa," called Jimmie to Lily as he tightened the reins and slowed her down from a trot to a walk.

"Come inside!" shouted the man. "They want to speak to you down at the fairground."

Jimmie stared in amazement. *Speak* to him? At the fairground—from the Town Hall? Why, the fairground was three miles out of town!

Then Jimmie remembered hearing about the new machine to be shown that year at the fair. He liked new machines and inventions, and he had intended to try the talking box when he went back to the fair that afternoon. This must be what he was to talk into now!

Jimmie stopped Lily. He jumped out of the buggy and tied her to a hitching post. Then he followed the man into the basement of the Town Hall. On the wall hung a strange-looking box with two black tubes fastened to it.

The man picked up one tube and held it to his ear. "HELLO," he shouted into the other tube.

Then he put the tubes into Jimmie's hands and pulled him toward the box.

"You listen *there,* and you talk into *that,*" the man whispered excitedly.

Jimmie held the black thing against his ear and listened. At first there was only a murmuring and a rumble. Then a voice came.

"Hello," the black tube said. "Oh, hello, is that Jimmie Marshall?"

"Yes," shouted Jimmie in amazement. How did the thing know his name?

For a minute there were only dim sounds that Jimmie could not understand. Then the words came clearly again.

"Your mother says to come back as fast as you can. Do you hear?"

"Yes," shouted Jimmie.

"Be back by half-past ten," said the voice from the tube.

"It's nearly ten now," thought Jimmie.

The voice went on, "Go home and get your s——" But Jimmie could not make out what he was to get, because suddenly there came a crash as the storm broke about him. It did not sound so loud to Jimmie as it did to Nan and her mother at the fairground, for the lightning had struck the elm tree just outside the fairground gate. Jimmie was three miles away, but the crash was loud enough to make him jump.

When he took up the tube again, not a sound could he get out of it. "I don't know what they want me to bring from home," cried Jimmie, "but whatever it is, it's got to be there in half an hour."

"You'd better hurry on home and see if you can discover what they want," suggested the man by the telephone.

Jimmie tore across the sidewalk, with the rain running down the back of his neck. He untied Lily, who was thoroughly wet and miserable, and climbed into the buggy.

"Poor old Lily, there's no dry stable for you yet," said Jimmie sympathetically as the nervous animal attempted to head for her stall in the town livery stable. Firmly but gently he turned her away from the livery stable and toward the Marshall house.

There was no one at home. Jimmie had to solve the riddle alone. What was it they wanted? Was it his mother's purse? He ran upstairs and looked in the top bureau drawer. No purse was there. Was it the lunch basket? He peered out of the window to see if it had been left on the porch. It was not to be seen. Could it be Nan's quilt? He ran to the guest room. There lay the quilt on the bed, wrapped neatly in a sheet!

"That's it," cried Jimmie triumphantly. "That's what Mother wants me to bring out to the fairground by ten-thirty!"

He put on a rubber coat. "Mackintoshes," people called them. Then he wrapped Nan's quilt in his father's mackintosh and hurried out into the storm, carrying his bundle carefully.

Under the hood of the buggy Jimmie kept as dry as possible. The rain beat down, and it was hard at times to be sure that he was keeping Lily on the road. But there was no time to be lost. Lily was a good horse, and they'd make it yet. The downpour was lessening, and the black cloud was moving away as swiftly as it had come.

Lily looked wild-eyed and frightened. She had never had a day like this before! But into the fairground they came at last. Jimmie hitched Lily as quickly as he could and carried the quilt into the big exhibit hall.

The clock on the grandstand was just striking the half-hour. The storm was over. The people were coming cautiously from cover.

When Mrs. Marshall saw Jimmie, she hardly believed her eyes. Nan jumped up and down, crying, "Did you bring the quilt? Did you bring the quilt?"

"Yes," Jimmie assured her. "I took it right over to the booth." Then nothing would do but they must all go to see it. There it was, labeled:

PATCHWORK QUILT PIECED BY
NAN MARSHALL—AGED 8 YEARS, 6 MONTHS

Later the judges came by and examined each bit of needlework. At last one of them reached over and put a blue ribbon on Nan's quilt.

Nan gave a sigh of happiness. First prize! And the telephone had helped her win it. She decided that she liked newfangled notions after all.

130

The Horseless Carriage

On the first day of the school vacation in the summer of 1894, Terry Randall sat at supper in his home in Kokomo, Indiana. He had eaten his ham and biscuits and had finished up the applesauce. Now he was impatient to get out to play a couple of innings of back-yard baseball before dark. But it did not look as if supper would ever be finished, for his father and the boarder, Mr. Haynes, were arguing about "Progress" again.

Grown-ups were always talking about progress. For fifty years invention had followed invention. Steam engines crossed land and sea. Gas and oil, the food for machines, had been found. Electricity

shot through wires, carrying messages even underneath the Atlantic Ocean. Mr. Haynes was full of interesting information about these new discoveries. He knew all about machinery, too. He knew how engines worked and what made pistons go up and down in a different direction from that of the wheels they were turning. He also knew about electricity and the way it ran along a piece of wire. And about gaslight, of course, since that was the reason Mr. Haynes was in town.

He had come to lay a pipe line so that people in Kokomo could cook with natural gas, and light the streets and houses with it. In the daytime he rode around the countryside, getting ready for the laying of the pipe line. At night he retired to his room and tinkered on his inventions.

Mr. Haynes was a wonderful man. He was always getting "parts" sent in by express, or asking Terry to stop at Mr. Apperson's blacksmith shop for a roll of wire or a piece of iron rod. His room was fairly littered with unfinished contraptions.

"And they're likely to stay unfinished," Terry's father had been heard to remark. He meant no disrespect to his boarder. He admired him very much. But it stood to reason, Mr. Randall always said, that there were limits to the ingenuity of man. "Even of Americans," he would add proudly, for Mr. Randall was extremely patriotic. Then he would go on to name the new inventions that had come into use just in the last century—railroads, gas and electric lights, telegraph, talking machines, telephones. "And that's all," Terry's father would say. "We've gone far enough. There won't be any more changes after today."

But the disapproval of Terry's father had not kept Mr. Haynes from tinkering away in all his spare time. He was trying to make a self-propelling buggy. He had a lot of traveling to do in the country, and his horse always seemed to wear out before the end of the day. "A vehicle that can go without being pulled by a horse is what I really need," he was saying at the supper table.

"A horseless carriage?" The very idea annoyed Mr. Randall. "It can't be done," he snorted, "and if it could, it would be perfectly useless. What are horses and railroads for? Anyway, something of the sort was tried in England, and it was so noisy that a man had to walk ahead with a red flag to warn drivers to keep tight hold of their horses."

"That was a steam vehicle," Mr. Haynes said mildly. "I'm not planning to use a steam engine. I thought of it, but a steam engine is too heavy, and I'd have to stop every mile or so to fix the fire and get steam up. I also thought of using electric batteries. A man in Paris, France, tried that, but electricity is too expensive to compete with steam."

Terry wished that Mr. Haynes would stop talking. It would soon be too dark to play ball.

"I've ordered a gasoline motor from an engine company in Michigan," went on Mr. Haynes. "A one-horsepowered gasoline engine."

All at once Terry remembered what Mr. Hollins, the stationmaster, had said that morning while Terry was at the depot to watch old No. 703 pull in. Leaning forward, he entered the conversation.

"Your engine has come, Mr. Haynes. It's down at the depot. Mr. Hollins says it's so big you'll have to fetch it home in a dray!"

Mr. Haynes went off immediately to get hold of a horse and cart. When he came back with his engine, Terry and Mr. Randall helped him carry it inside. But where was he to put it? It weighed one hundred eighty pounds. Taking it upstairs to his room was out of the question.

"The kitchen is the biggest room in the house," Terry ventured to suggest timidly.

"I always did want to see how these inventions came about," said Terry's mother. "I'll be glad to have Mr. Haynes put his engine in my kitchen, where I can keep an eye on it." She made room for the strange contraption in one corner.

Then Mr. Haynes wanted to find out how much power would be needed from the gears for the engine to pull the buggy. "Testing the traction," he

called it. So he got Terry to fasten his bicycle to
the buggy and tow it up Maple Street. And when
Mr. Apperson came out from his blacksmith shop,
they made the test all over again for him to see.

For the next few days, whenever Terry went by
Mr. Apperson's, he would see the blacksmith working on something for Mr. Haynes' machine. When
Terry went to the depot to meet the trains, people
would ask, "How's the invention?"

Everyone in town was interested except Terry's
father, who was working hard on a speech for the
Fourth of July celebration. One of his ancestors
had signed the Declaration of Independence. That
made it seem proper for Mr. Randall to read the
Declaration at public gatherings.

The night before the Fourth, Mr. Haynes pulled his buggy to the back yard, and Mr. Apperson came over to help him. They lifted the motor into a frame they had made and fastened the gears and levers next to the hand brake. Terry stood around and watched. They all saw Mr. Hollins come to the front door and speak to Mr. Randall. But they did not think about his being a deputy constable, as well as stationmaster, until the next day when everyone was ready for the picnic.

Mr. Haynes had got all dressed up in his striped pants and a stiff straw hat with a brown and purple hatband. Terry followed him out to the yard where the buggy was standing. To Terry's surprise, Mr. Hollins, the stationmaster, was in the yard, too. He stepped up and pulled out his constable's badge.

"You can't take that contraption on the streets of Kokomo!" he said.

"The streets are free, aren't they?" Mr. Haynes retorted.

"Sure, they're free. What's that got to do with it?"

"Go listen to the Declaration of Independence and you'll see what it has to do with it. All men are created equal with certain inalienable rights. And among these are life, liberty, and the pursuit of happiness. Liberty's made up of all sorts of little things, Mr. Hollins. And the pursuit of happiness is more important than people let on for it to be. America's a big country. How are we going to get about it with an old-fashioned animal like a horse that gets worn out before the day is gone?"

"There's the railroad," Mr. Hollins said, forgetting that some old fogies had tried to stop the railroad, too, when it was first started.

"The railroad is fine for where it goes," said Mr. Haynes. "But what about little side roads? What about going somewhere the railroad doesn't go?"

Mr. Hollins looked very uncomfortable. "I tell you what," he said, wiping beads of perspiration off his forehead. "I can't let you start driving a horseless vehicle on the streets of Kokomo because some people have objected to it, but you could pull the buggy out of town where I have no authority. Then if you happened to come riding back to town again, I don't see how I could stop you—not if the engine does what you say it will. I don't see how anything in Kokomo would be swift enough to stop you at all."

"I could hitch the horse to the buggy. But how would I get the horse home?" Mr. Haynes asked.

"How about the Randall boy? Couldn't he go and bring the horse back?" suggested Mr. Hollins.

That was how it happened that Terry Randall set out with Mr. Haynes for the crossroads three miles out in the country. Away they went in a buggy with a gasoline engine fastened under it, all ready to run by itself when given the chance!

At the crossroads Mr. Haynes did not talk and neither did Terry. They unhitched the Randalls' horse and buckled on his saddle. Next they took the shafts off the buggy and turned it around to face Kokomo. Then they poured a can of gasoline into the tank underneath, and there the thing was, waiting to go traveling. Terry felt rather queer. The buggy without the horse looked so small and lonesome there in the road.

Mr. Haynes must have thought the same thing because he said, "Maybe she won't work. Maybe it's not possible. But anyhow——"

Swallowing hard, he did not finish his sentence. He jumped into the buggy and set the levers for starting. Then he climbed down again and got his crank. He fitted it into the part of the engine that was set between the wheels and gave the crank a quick twirl.

"I'd take you along," he said to Terry, "but the ride might be dangerous."

It seemed at the moment that indeed it might be. There came a sputter and a cough and a great chugging like that of a railroad engine. A trail of smoke came out at the back of the vehicle. Then the noise stopped, and the little buggy stood helpless once more in the road between the cornfields.

Mr. Haynes spun the crank again. There came another sputter and a chug. This time he jumped into the seat, grabbed the steering stick, and fed gas to the motor before it could stop again.

"You'd better hold the horse," he called to Terry. The wheels began turning, and the buggy lurched forward. "Come down to the picnic. I'll *try* to stop there."

The rest of Mr. Haynes' words were lost in the uproar. Down the road in a column of dust went the amazing vehicle, with nothing to pull it except some machinery that was fastened with wire under the seat and hitched somehow to the wheels.

Terry rode the horse at a gallop, but he did not see Mr. Haynes again until he arrived at the picnic ground back of the courthouse. There in the center of an awe-struck crowd was the horseless buggy. It was dust-covered and smoky, but it looked as if it knew that it had done something pretty fine.

"Buggymobile, that's what you ought to call it," somebody said to the inventor. "Why, it just went *tearing* up the street. It must have been going *ten miles an hour!*"

Then Terry's teacher, who was always spouting poetry, remarked, "When Mr. Haynes came riding up, I said to myself, ''Tis well to borrow from the good and great. 'Tis wise to learn; 'tis Godlike to create.'"

"The engine stayed in my kitchen," said someone, and Terry saw his mother, very stylish in her best starched white shirtwaist dress. She spoke in a low voice, but Terry could see she took pride in her boarder's accomplishment. Terry looked around for his father, wondering what he would say.

Mr. Randall was still on the speaker's stand, but he was nodding his head the way he always did when something pleased him.

Mr. Haynes waved to Terry's father. "If it hadn't been for the Randalls, I couldn't have built my machine," he declared. "And I'd be honored if Mr. Randall would take a short ride around the town with me. There will be room for Terry, too. I don't believe there is any danger now, though of course it's still too risky for the ladies."

Terry's father folded up his speech and put it in his pocket carefully. He had not finished it, but no one remembered that now. Maybe someone would remember after the picnic and ask him to finish the reading of the Declaration. He had gotten only as far as the words "life, liberty, and the pursuit of happiness."

Mr. Randall climbed into the buggy and clutched the sides firmly. Terry squeezed close to him to leave room on the seat for Mr. Haynes. The crank was turned. The spark caught, and the explosion sounded immediately.

Mr. Haynes leaped nimbly into the driver's seat and caught hold of the steering stick. They started down the main street, with a shouting, cheering crowd behind them.

Near the railroad station they met Mr. Hollins walking determinedly toward them. He had pinned his constable's badge on his coat, and they could see that he meant to take some action, however reluctantly. He was about to step into the road and halt the buggy when Terry's father waved him out of the way with a gesture of authority.

"It's all right, Hollins," said Mr. Randall. "I've changed my mind about this buggy. If gasoline

vehicles are going to be invented, Kokomo might as well get the credit!"

After they had gone on a little farther, he spoke again, slowly and thoughtfully. And if Terry had not been squeezed in so close to him, it is doubtful if he could have heard his father's words.

"I guess we have to get used to the idea that America is always going to be thinking up something new," said Mr. Randall.

From out the Christmas Skies

The room was bright with yellow light from the lamp on the center table, and with firelight glowing through the windows of a fat black stove. In one corner Danny Warren was making clicking sounds on a small instrument. His father, with earphones on his head, was sitting before the wireless set he had made himself. Mrs. Warren and Peggy were stringing popcorn chains for the Christmas tree.

The clock on the shelf chimed.

"Oh, my," said Mrs. Warren. "It's eight o'clock. Tomorrow is Christmas Eve, and there's still so much to do. Daniel Warren, I should think you and your father could both find something better to do than play with those old wireless things!"

"Great things are going to come from wireless, Mama," said Mr. Warren. "Great things! Why, when Daniel was a baby, a man named Marconi tapped out the first wireless message in Italy. He sent it for a whole mile without wires!

"And just four years ago—four years, mind you, Mama—a wireless message came through the air clear across the Atlantic Ocean. When Danny is grown up, who knows what wonderful things will come through the air? It is good for him to play with the telegraph key and learn the Morse Code. Then he can understand these wonderful things."

"Sure!" exclaimed Danny. "And maybe some-day we'll fly around in the sky and hear messages up in the clouds."

"Papa," Peggy spoke up abruptly, "Daisy Grant's father has a new Ford automobile! Some of the children in school laughed when they heard about it. But, Papa, I thought about you and——"

"What then, Peggy?" asked Mr. Warren gently.

"I got up and said, 'You let Daisy alone! Her papa has sense. He's like mine. He knows that if you don't believe in anything new, you never get anything better than what you have.'"

"Why, what a fine speech!" cried Mrs. Warren.

Even Daniel looked at his sister with respect. Usually he thought that girls were just girls. They didn't understand the need for new inventions.

"That was a fine thing for you to do, Peggy," praised Mr. Warren.

Then he turned to his wife. "There's a rumor that something special is going to be sent over the wireless tomorrow night. It's to come from Brant Rock, Massachusetts. That is over two hundred miles away from us here in Pennsylvania!"

"Something special? What do you mean?" asked Mrs. Warren. "Isn't it just dot-dash, dot-dash, dot-dash, like the telegraph?"

"Code, Mama," Mr. Warren corrected her.

"All right, *code*," she said, her dimples showing.

"It might be a speech," Mr. Warren continued. "They've been trying to send voices. Well, whatever it is, I won't get to hear it. I have to be at the telegraph board at the railroad office tomorrow night."

"You mean you can't listen, even if it's special?" exclaimed Danny. "Why don't you ask Mr. Major to change places with you?"

"Can't ask a man to take my place on Christmas Eve," replied Mr. Warren. "Anyway, Ed Major thinks I'm crazy because I tinker with a wireless set. Ed's as up to date as George Washington's hat. He wants everything just as it's always been."

"Well," said his wife, "no matter what Ed thinks, I do wish you might hear your special program tomorrow night."

145

The next day Mr. Warren slept late to be ready for his night work at the telegraph board. But the rest of the family got up early. Danny carried the Christmas tree into the parlor, and Peggy brought in the box of ornaments. They worked as quietly as possible so as not to wake Mr. Warren, though sometimes giggles and whoops did pop out.

"I wish Papa would ask Mr. Major to take his place tonight," sighed Mrs. Warren as she strung cranberries for the tree. "I know how much he wants to listen to that 'something special' over the wireless."

Peggy had an inspiration. "Well, *we* could ask him even if Papa won't!" she said excitedly.

"I don't think Papa would want us to," replied her mother. "But I must say I'm tempted. Mr. Major has no family. It probably wouldn't matter to him if he had to work on Christmas Eve."

"Let me ask him, Ma," begged Danny.

His mother shook her head. "No, you'd better not. Papa wouldn't want you to say anything."

By ten o'clock the tree was decorated. It stood bright and piney-smelling in the sunshine that came through the big bay window. Then Mrs. Warren sent the children on an errand. When it was done, Danny announced, "Peg, I'm going on down to the railroad station to talk to Mr. Major."

"Oh, Danny, you mustn't!" cried Peggy, aghast at the thought. "Mama doesn't want us to go down to the railroad office. The men are too busy."

"Well," Danny replied, "Papa wants to listen tonight, and I'm going to help him. You should, too. You stood up for Daisy. Now you have to stand up for Papa."

Peggy's eyes widened with surprise at this new thought. "Why, of course I'll stand up for Papa! I'll come, Danny."

In no time the two youngsters were down at the railroad station. Mr. Major looked up from his telegraph keyboard and grinned good-naturedly.

"What's your pa doing?" he asked. "Tuning in his wireless to hear Mars?"

Danny returned the grin. "He's asleep, and he doesn't know we've come to see you. He wouldn't want us to."

Mr. Major looked surprised. "Something wrong at your house?" he asked with concern.

"Oh, no," said Danny hurriedly. "But we came to ask you—would you please—would you work in Papa's place tonight?"

"Please, Mr. Major," Peggy chimed in. "You know Papa thinks the air is full of secrets, and he is expecting something marvelous over the wireless tonight. He doesn't know what it is, but he's heard it's to be something special. Please let him hear it, Mr. Major!"

"Your pa's got fancy notions. Nothing's coming over the air but some more dots and dashes. I'd think he would get tired of listening to them. But I'll do it. Tell your pa to come this afternoon so I can have time off for a nap and some supper."

"Oh, thank you, Mr. Major," breathed Danny and Peggy together. "Thank you!" They ran home to tell the wonderful news.

"Children," their mother scolded as they bounded in the door, "it's past lunchtime. Where have you been?"

Danny and Peggy could hear their father moving about in the next room, getting dressed.

"Papa, Papa," they shouted. "Mr. Major says you should come to work this afternoon, and then he'll work for you tonight."

"Children!" Mrs. Warren's voice was stern.

But neither she nor her husband could be really cross. They were both too pleased to know that Mr. Warren could listen to his wireless.

That evening the family had supper in the parlor by the Christmas tree. Then Mr. Warren went to his wireless set and adjusted his earphones. He waited for the familiar code, perhaps some call for help on the sea, or a Christmas message. Mrs. Warren went over to the window and rolled up the shade to the very top.

"The sky is glorious tonight," she said.

Mr. Warren took off his earphones and went to look. "Put on your coats," he said. "Let's step outside a moment."

"But your wireless, Papa!" worried Danny.

"There is nothing on it yet," his father replied. "We'll be back in a few minutes."

The whole family walked slowly around the block in the starlit December night. Neighbors called to them gaily, and on a corner stood a group singing Christmas carols.

"How lovely the music sounds!" murmured Mrs. Warren as they stopped to listen.

"Papa shouldn't be away from his wireless for so long," Danny whispered anxiously to Peggy.

"No, but Mama is enjoying the walk so much," Peggy answered softly.

The family stood for a few minutes more while Mrs. Warren continued to listen with delight. The children could see that their father was growing impatient, though he said nothing. To Danny and Peggy it seemed a long time before they let themselves once more into their warm house.

Mr. Warren looked quickly at the clock. "Thirty minutes I've been gone! Thirty minutes!" Going to the wireless set, he snatched up his earphones.

Then he stood as motionless as a statue in the park. He seemed to be listening with his whole body.

"Mama! Children!" he called in a shaky voice after a moment of spellbound silence. "Come and listen!"

He fastened the headpiece over his wife's brown hair. Her eyes grew wide and startled.

"There's music!" she cried delightedly. "Danny and Peggy! You must hear it, too."

First Danny listened, and then Peggy.

"Music," she repeated breathlessly. "Music in the air. There's a violin playing 'O Holy Night!' Now a man's singing it. I can hardly believe it!"

"But where from, Papa?" asked Danny.

"From Brant Rock," replied his father. "I told you something special was coming from there."

Mr. Warren listened again and said, "A voice is speaking this time." He repeated the message to his family. "'Glory to God in the highest, and on earth peace, and good will toward men.'"

Mr. Warren's eyes, usually so merry, were very serious now. "Children, do you realize we have heard music sent through the air for the first time? Up in Massachusetts, more than two hundred miles from here, a man picked up a violin and played a Christmas carol for us. We sat snugly at home in our little cottage and heard it all."

"Music in the skies on Christmas Eve," sighed Mrs. Warren happily.

"Quick, call Mr. Major!" begged Peggy.

Her father went to the wall telephone and wound the handle. "Hello, Central? The railroad station, please. . . . Hello, Wallace, Merry Christmas. Let me speak to Ed, please. . . . Ed? It was music on the wireless, Ed. I knew there was going to be something special. . . . Music! A violin playing 'O Holy Night!' . . . What's that you say, Ed?"

Dan and Peggy could not hear what Mr. Major said, but something in their father's face told them that Mr. Major would never again joke about the wireless. He would think, as all the Warrens did, that the music in the air had been a real Christmas miracle. A miracle that would bring pleasure and benefits to the whole world!

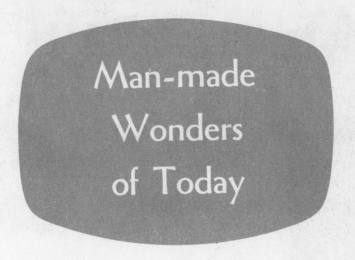

Man-made
Wonders
of Today

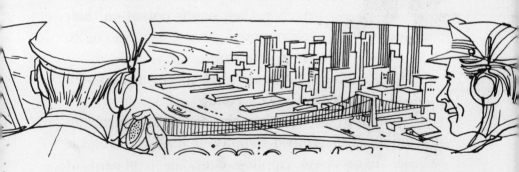

Trials of a Trio

"Ready?" asked Casey Bowman, tapping the sheet music in his hand.

Quick nods from Ted and David Archer, their hands poised on their instruments, gave Casey his cue to start counting.

"One . . . two . . . three." Each boy thumped a foot in time with Casey's count.

Strumming the opening chords of the music on his guitar, Ted grinned happily at his twin brother, whose fingers were rippling over the keyboard of his accordion. After the first few bars Casey took a step forward and began to sing.

"Let's try it again," said Casey when the song was finished. "Today's Wednesday. We've only two more days before our audition Saturday morning. And we need a lot of practice to be smooth enough to get on that radio talent show."

"Don't fret, boy," Ted said, plucking the guitar strings lazily. "With your mellow voice, David's accordion, and my guitar, who can beat us? We're in, Casey! Relax!"

Nevertheless the trio rehearsed the song twice more before ending their practice session in the Archers' garage. The audition meant a great deal to the boys, who had formed their trio a year ago. After months of faithful practicing, they had finally decided that they were good enough to try out for a talent program that was broadcast from their city. Together they had written to the program director, describing their act and asking for an opportunity to show what they could do.

Last Monday the boys had received an answering letter from the program director. To their joy they were invited to appear at the radio station for an audition at nine-thirty the next Saturday morning. The letter said further that if the act had sufficient merit, the trio would be given an opportunity three weeks later to appear on the weekly talent show. The trio would then take its chances with the other chosen contestants.

Thursday was a damp, cold November day. The trio practiced after school as usual in the Archers' heated garage.

This time David's fingers did not seem quite so nimble on the accordion. He went over the music several times by himself, repeating the most difficult passages until his face was wet with perspiration. Casey was having his troubles, too. He could not remember the words of the song. He had sung it at least fifty times that week, but today the words would not stick in his mind.

All three of the boys worked conscientiously and determinedly. By the time they quit, they felt that they were note- and word-perfect.

"I'm getting jumpy," Ted admitted.

"I am, too," said Casey. "I hope I don't muff those words at the audition."

"Don't worry about it," David said encouragingly. "You're just suffering from stage fright."

"I hope so," Casey muttered. He pulled on his coat and opened the side door of the garage. At once a sharp gust of wind slammed the door back against the wall. "Wow!" yelled Casey. "Quite a storm blew up while we were rehearsing. Everything's covered with ice."

"Take it easy," Ted cautioned.

"I will," said Casey. "So long till tomorrow." Stepping outside, he pushed the garage door shut.

The twins finished putting away their instruments and hurried into the house. "Time to clean up for dinner, boys," called their mother. "It's almost ready."

Later, as the family were eating the last of their ice cream, the telephone rang.

"I'll get it," Ted said, hurrying to the telephone in the hall. "Maybe it's Casey with a new idea for the trio."

But it was Casey's father.

"I have some bad news for you, Ted," said Mr. Bowman, recognizing the boy's voice. "I'm at the hospital with Casey. He slipped on the ice in front of our house and broke his leg. I called the doctor, and we brought him to the hospital right away. I'm afraid he will have to stay here for at least ten days."

"B-b-but——" Ted sputtered in shocked surprise.

"I know," interrupted Mr. Bowman. "You are thinking of that audition on Saturday. Casey is more worried about that than about his broken leg. But I don't know what to do about it. If you boys figure out something, let me know. I'll help you in any way I can. Good-by."

Ted hung up and sat for a minute staring at the telephone. Then he went slowly back to the dining room to break the news. "There goes our chance for the talent show," he said dejectedly.

There was a dismayed silence. Then David said doubtfully, "Maybe we can find a way out."

"How?" jeered Ted. "We're a trio, remember? Casey's singing gives our act its sparkle. Without him we're nothing. And we certainly couldn't get anybody to take his place in such a short time."

Ted slumped down on his chair. "I wish we had a record of today's practice session. Maybe we could have used that for our radio tryout."

"I'm sure a record would not be accepted," said Mr. Archer thoughtfully. "But you've given me an idea. By tomorrow night I may have a way to help you solve your problem."

No amount of wheedling could make him explain his idea, but the twins went to bed that night in a more hopeful frame of mind.

Early the next morning they called Casey at the hospital. Though he said that he felt all right, he sounded weak and depressed.

"Cheer up, Casey," said David. "Dad thinks he may have a way to help us. We'll know tonight."

When Ted and David returned from school that afternoon, they were surprised to find their father waiting for them. He was smiling broadly.

"Well, boys," he announced, "I have something that may help you go through with your audition. See this box? I brought it from the office. It's a tape recorder."

With a flourish Mr. Archer threw open the lid of the case, disclosing a machine with two reels connected by a narrow tape. The tape wound around one reel, passed through a recording device, and then wound around the other reel. In one corner was a hand microphone that was attached to the machine by a six-foot cord.

"This machine can record sounds on tape and then play them back with amazing exactness," Mr. Archer explained enthusiastically. "We often use it in our office."

"You mean we can put our trio on tape?" Ted exclaimed eagerly. Then his face fell: "But if we can't use a phonograph record of our act for the audition, how can we use a tape recording?"

"Oh, I didn't mean a tape recording of the whole trio," said his father. "I'm sure that wouldn't be acceptable. But if you boys go to the studio and explain the circumstances to the program director, he may let you play your instruments with Casey's voice dubbed in from the tape recorder. After all, there will be only a small audience listening to the audition.. If you assure the director that Casey can appear in person on the talent show, the tape recording may be allowed just for the audition."

David and Ted smiled gratefully at their father. "That's a mighty clever idea!" cried Ted. "Let's get that recording right away."

After consulting Casey's father, the two boys and Mr. Archer drove off to the hospital. In the back seat of the car was the apparatus they would need, the tape recorder and the twins' instruments.

At the hospital Mr. Archer spoke to Casey's doctor. It was agreed that the boy's condition would not prevent his singing.

"In fact," the doctor added, "singing might help Casey considerably. Nothing was ever lower than that boy's spirit when he found out that he would have to miss the audition."

Upstairs in Casey's room everyone began talking at once. But finally the idea of using the tape recorder was made clear to Casey. His face grew excited and happy. "I hope it works!" he cried.

"Give me a minute to practice, and I'll be all set."
Propped up in bed, he cleared his throat and sang
a few scales.

Mr. Archer looked up from plugging the recorder
into the room's electrical outlet. "Casey, take as
much time as you need. Ted can accompany you
at first on the guitar. But you'll have to sing without any help when we make the audition recording."

"I understand, Mr. Archer," Casey replied as he
took the microphone David handed him. "We're
ready now. Turn on that machine."

Ted softly strummed the opening chords of the
melody. Then he nodded at Casey to give him his
cue, and Casey joined in with the words.

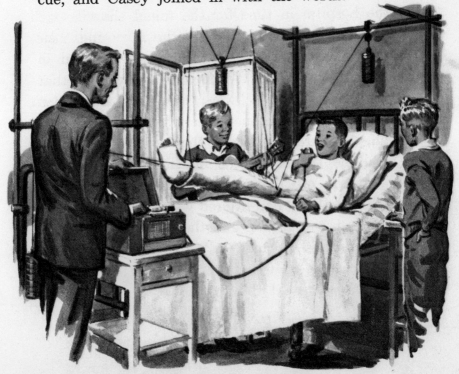

After the first few measures Casey flatted and began to muff the words.

"I'm sorry," he said ruefully.

"Relax, Casey," Ted told him, smiling.

The next try went better. Then Casey sang the song twice without Ted's accompanying guitar.

"Once more if you're not too tired," Mr. Archer suggested. "We should have several trials to take with us. Then the twins will have a choice when they put your voice and their music together."

Casey sang again. "I think that's enough," said Mr. Archer when the boy had finished. "Now get some rest, Casey. I'm sure that the trio is going to have a successful audition, so you must be out of the hospital in time for the talent show."

Back at the Archers' house, the boys and their father set to work. First Mr. Archer plugged in the tape recorder and switched on the control that set the tape going backward, to rewind it. When the tape reached the point at which the recording began, Mr. Archer stopped the rewinding.

Then he turned on the machine. Immediately the first trial of Casey's song could be heard. Each sound that Casey had uttered was reproduced faithfully—even the flatting and the muffing of words—as well as Casey's and Ted's remarks.

"We'll erase that first try from the tape later," Mr. Archer assured the boys.

Now the second trial could be heard. This time Casey's voice was clearer and stronger, and the next three trials showed still more improvement. The twins agreed that the last try was the best.

"You two get ready with your instruments while I rewind the tape," said Mr. Archer. "The first four tries will be automatically erased after I click this button."

In a few minutes the tape was clear except for Casey's last trial. At a nod from their father, the boys counted, "One . . . two . . . three," and started to play. At the same instant Mr. Archer quietly switched on the tape recorder to give the machine time to warm up during the opening bars of music. But his timing was not quite right. Casey's voice came in a few seconds too late.

"Let's try again," said Ted eagerly, interrupting the song. "That wasn't far off."

On the third attempt Mr. Archer's timing was perfect. Exactly on beat Casey's voice sang out, clear and warm, as if the singer himself were in the room.

Mr. Archer gave the boys a triumphant grin.

That evening after dinner they practiced again and again to make sure that Mr. Archer could dub in Casey's voice at the right moment. Each time the voice came out sharply, without any blurring from the frequent use of the tape.

Early on Saturday morning the "trio" rehearsed once more. Then the twins called Casey to tell him how successfully their father had dubbed in the voice recording.

"We're leaving for the radio station right now," David added excitedly.

In the audition studio they asked their way to the program director, Mr. Goodhue. David and Ted were carrying their instruments. Mr. Archer had the tape recorder.

"Are you the trio?" the director asked them in surprise. "I got the impression from your letter that you were all about the same age."

"We are," laughed Ted. "This is our father. The other member of the trio isn't here."

"Well," said Mr. Goodhue, looking at his watch, "it's about time for your act. I hope your missing partner arrives soon."

"He can't be here," David spoke up. "But his voice is! Dad, you tell him about it, please."

Smiling, Mr. Archer explained the situation.

The director stared at the two youngsters a bit doubtfully. "You're sure that your singer will be available for the radio show if we approve your trio today?" he asked. "Otherwise, there isn't any point to this audition. We couldn't let you use a tape recording on the talent show instead of the real singer. That wouldn't be fair, of course, to the other contestants."

"Oh, Casey will be out of the hospital by then," the boys said positively, "though he'll be hobbling around on crutches."

"All right, then," said the director. "Take your places on that platform over there and get ready. When I give you a nod, begin."

Ted and David followed their father nervously to the platform. Once the boys stumbled in confusion over some studio microphone wires, almost dropping their instruments. Finally the guitar was out of its case, the accordion was strapped to David's shoulders, and the tape recorder was plugged into a nearby outlet. Then the boys saw Mr. Goodhue looking in their direction.

The audition was about to begin! Both the boys
moistened their lips with a momentary sensation of
panic, but a wink from their father steadied them.

The director gave a curt nod. David tapped his
foot, one . . . two . . . three. From the studio
microphones came the rhythmic beat of the melody,
joined at the proper time by Casey's voice. The
audition went off without a hitch.

As the relieved boys grinned at their father, the
program director approached. "Your trio is tops,"
he said. "We'll save a spot for you on our radio
talent show three weeks from next Thursday. If
your singer can sing that well from a hospital bed,
he must be terrific standing on his feet!"

I'd Like to Be a Lighthouse

I'd like to be a lighthouse
   All scrubbed and painted white.
I'd like to be a lighthouse
   And stay awake all night
To keep my eye on everything
   That sails my patch of sea;
I'd like to be a lighthouse
   With the ships all watching me.

Coast Guard to the Rescue

Jim Brewster felt a sharp thrill run up and down his spine. Here he was, droning along at 1000 feet over the world's busiest harbor, copilot of a Coast Guard plane! He looked down at the vast reach of the Atlantic far below. On the starboard side, on the water, he could see the shadow of his plane racing along slightly ahead of the plane itself. He sighed contentedly.

The pilot, Lieutenant Curt Sprong, circled over docks where ships were taking on cargoes. Then, heading north, he flew up the Hudson River above the towering skyline of New York.

Here there were many vessels to observe: ferries shuttling back and forth, toylike tugboats chugging importantly about their business, fuel barges, and other harbor craft—all weaving in and out. Not a single ship nor a single small powerboat escaped the keen eyes of the two pilots of the Coast Guard plane. As usual, on a training flight such as this, the plane carried its regular crew of two pilots, a radioman, and a mechanic.

Just as the pilot was about to ask the radioman to report that they were coming in, a radio message came from the Coast Guard station on Long Island.

"Two boys in a sailboat off Indian Head Inlet," the message said. "We are requested to find out if they need help."

By the time the radioman had acknowledged the report, Curt had found the inlet on the map. He wheeled the big seaplane around. Dropping down to 500 feet, he swung the ship onto a course over the south shore of Long Island.

"Looks plenty rough down there," Jim said to his fellow flight officer.

"About three feet from crest to crest, I'd say," the pilot judged. "Keep your eye peeled for those boys. Wonder how they happened to go out on a day like this."

Both men kept a close watch on the coves and inlets that unfolded below them as they sped on.

"See anything?" Curt asked.

"No—not yet. Wait—now I do!" Jim exclaimed. "Looks like a small sailboat turned bottom up."

Curt brought the plane down to within a hundred feet of the water and circled around the capsized boat to come into the wind. Now he could clearly see the boys clinging desperately to their boat as it neared the breakers.

"There's a boat trying to reach them!" Jim said.

Two men in a skiff were doing their best to row out to the boys, who were about a hundred feet offshore. But each time the rescuers headed into the breakers, the waves caught their boat and hurled it back. As Jim watched, the skiff almost capsized, too. "It'll never reach those boys!" Jim shouted. "We'd better radio the Coast Guard helicopter."

"We can't wait," Curt said. Ordering the crew to prepare for a landing, he put the plane into a glide. With the stick hard back and the flaps down, he let the ship down onto the rough sea.

The plane smacked the first wave hard and then bounced to the next one. But the severity of the second contact was lessened by the way the pilot worked the throttles during the split second that the plane was in the air between waves.

As Curt deftly worked the seaplane toward the overturned boat, Jim climbed onto the hull. In his hand he held a coiled line and a life preserver ready to toss to the boys. In the distance he noticed that

the skiff was holding off. Apparently the would-be
rescuers realized that the Coast Guard plane had
a better chance than they to save the two boys.

"Hang on, boys!" Curt called out.

But the victims were too weak to reply. Each
buffeting wave threatened to break their hold.

"Grab this line when I throw it," Jim shouted
above the sound of wind and waves.

As soon as he felt sure that the older boy had
understood his order, Jim heaved the life preserver
through the air toward him. It shot over the boat,
which was now broadside to the plane, and slapped
down lightly beside the larger boy. The youngster
relaxed his grip on the overturned boat just long
enough to grab the life preserver and then slip his
companion's arms through it.

Jim pulled in the slack. "Make a try for it," he
shouted. "I'll help you."

The smaller boy slipped into the water, clinging
to the life preserver with his last ounce of strength.
He was pulled steadily toward the seaplane and was
soon alongside. Jim grabbed him under the arms
and pulled him aboard. The youngster was limp as
Jim lifted him up to the mechanic.

Once more Jim coiled the line. By this time the
plane had drifted farther from the capsized boat.

"Think you can make it?" Curt called to the
older boy as Jim again tossed the life preserver.

The line whistled through the air but fell short of the boy's position. To make matters worse, the boy stretched out his arm to grasp it and lost his hold on the boat. For a moment Jim thought that he would have to jump in for him. But the plucky lad swam to the life preserver and hooked his arm through it. Jim soon had him alongside.

Both boys were unconscious when they reached the safety of the seaplane's cabin. But they soon revived with the application of first-aid measures. Jim helped make them as comfortable and secure as possible for the take-off. "How do you feel, old timer?" he asked the smaller boy.

The youngster smiled weakly.

"I—I—guess I'm all right now," he replied.

Jim turned to the older boy. "You saved your chum's life," he said.

"Aw, that wasn't anything," answered the boy. "He's littler than I am. He couldn't have hung on much longer. I couldn't have either, I guess," he added. "Thanks, sir, for what you did."

Jim smiled and hurried forward for the take-off. Curt gunned his engines and lifted the ship into the air for the return flight. Calling the radioman, he directed him to have the station notify the boys' families that both lads were safe and were making for port. Then he put the big ship on the home course. The morning's work was finished.

Telephone in Motion

"I'm sorry you missed my letter, boys," said Mr. Lane to his nephews as he wiped his greasy hands on a paper towel. "I wrote you two days ago that your jobs would not be open this summer."

"But, Uncle Eric!" cried Phil, setting down his suitcase beside a gasoline pump. "Denny and I have been planning all year on helping you run your service station again this summer."

"Yes," Denny added, "we've been counting on this job for part of our school expenses."

The boys' uncle sighed unhappily. Regarding the deserted buildings across the lake, he said, "Ever since that army camp was abandoned, business has been falling off. About the only people who pass by are the ranchers who live on this road."

Mr. Lane was silent a moment. Then he went on, "I've decided to dispose of my property. You know I have five acres between the road and the lake. A man in Central City wants to buy them.

"But," Mr. Lane interrupted himself with a bleak smile, "we'll talk later. You chaps must be tired and hungry after that long bus trip. Go on to the house. Aunt Dolly will get you some supper."

Later, as the boys were preparing for bed, they talked the matter over. "There's surely something we can do to help Uncle Eric keep his station," Denny maintained stoutly.

"Maybe we'll think of something tomorrow," Phil replied. "Anyway, we can help Uncle Eric until he *does* sell, if he has to. Shall we work the way we did last year—take turns, two hours at a time? I can start right after breakfast."

"All right," agreed Denny. "Then I'll take over at ten o'clock."

The next morning Phil hurried out to the service station. Mr. Lane was leaning against the wall of the station, his hands sunk in his pockets.

"First shift reporting for duty!" Phil called out in what he hoped was a cheerful voice.

"Fine," replied his uncle. "Then I'll leave you in charge. There's not enough business for both of us, and I've something important to attend to."

The boy watched his uncle depart with a feeling of distress. Phil had plenty of time to worry, for it was just as Mr. Lane had said. Business was very bad.

Finally a car did stop. As Phil was wiping the windshield, he spoke to the rancher at the wheel. "Would you care if this service station closed up?" he asked.

"I certainly would," replied the man emphatically. "The gas that we use on the ranch is delivered by tank truck, but I'd have to drive forty-five miles to Webster Hollow to have my car greased and repaired. Is there a chance this station may close?"

When Phil told of his uncle's intentions, the man shook his head sympathetically. "That's too bad," he said. "Why not talk to the other ranchers who stop here? I'll see as many as I can. Maybe we can drum up more business for your uncle."

"Why, that's mighty kind of you, sir," Phil said gratefully.

By a quarter past nine, two more ranchers had stopped at the service station. Phil told each one the news. They, too, pledged their help in keeping the station open.

It was almost ten when a blue convertible rolled up to a gas pump. "My name is Swanson," the driver told Phil as the boy filled the gas tank. "I want to look at some land on the other side of the lake, and I need a guide. Do you know where I can hire somebody to drive me around who knows the roads over there? I'll pay ten dollars."

Phil thought quickly. Denny would be starting his shift in a few minutes. And ten dollars would certainly help toward school expenses.

"I can go with you," the boy offered, introducing himself. "I'll leave a note for my brother."

"Fine!" agreed Mr. Swanson. "I suppose you have a driver's license?"

"Sure." Phil scribbled a message on a paper towel and stuck it on a gas pump.

"Then get under the wheel," said Mr. Swanson, sliding over on the blue leather seat.

Heading for the wooded hills that bordered the lake, Phil gave himself over to the joy of driving the beautiful convertible. He had never seen a car with so many accessories. There were headlight visors, a spotlight, a six-foot antenna attached to the rear fender, and various other things.

But what interested Phil most was an object exactly like a telephone cradled in a special panel that was installed under the dashboard.

Mr. Swanson saw him glance at it. "That's a mobile telephone," he said. "It's a mighty big help in my business."

"You mean you can call somebody while you're riding?" asked Phil.

"If I'm not too far away from a mobile station, I can speak to anyone else who has a telephone—anywhere."

Phil was impressed. "I know some trucks have mobile telephones, but I've never seen one in an ordinary car."

When they reached the other side of the lake, Mr. Swanson had Phil stop the car several times while he stepped out and looked around at the hilly country. Soon they came to the buildings of the abandoned army camp. Mr. Swanson got out again and examined the buildings from all angles. He tapped the walls and took some measurements.

Meanwhile, Phil remained in the car and thought about his uncle's problems. Suddenly he sat bolt upright. He had forgotten to tell Denny about the ranchers' promises to help. He had better get back in a hurry. Someone might come along with a plan to keep the service station open.

Just then Mr. Swanson returned to the car. "I think I've seen enough for the present," he said. "We can go back now."

"Will we have to stop anywhere along the way?" Phil asked as he turned the car quickly.

"No," the man replied. Then he laughed. "You seem to be in a great hurry all of a sudden."

"I am," said Phil, and told about the plan to enlist the ranchers' help for Uncle Eric. "I forgot to tell my brother to talk to his customers about it. That's why I'm in a rush to get back."

"Don't worry," chuckled Mr. Swanson. "Your uncle's going to have plenty of business soon. My company sent me here to decide about buying those unused buildings for a year-round vacation resort.

My examination has convinced me that it's a sound idea. The buildings are in good shape, and we'll get established right away. Then people will be driving on this road all year long."

Phil almost whooped with relief and delight as he started back to the service station. "Won't you come in and meet my uncle?" he invited when they arrived.

"I'll stop on my way back," said Mr. Swanson, paying Phil the ten dollars. "There's a rancher up the road I want to see. I'll be back soon."

As Mr. Swanson drove away, Phil ran to find Denny. His brother was sitting inside the station, half asleep. Phil dashed in, yelling at the top of his voice.

"Say, what's got into you?" Denny asked with a startled look. "You act as if everything was just wonderful instead of the mess it really is."

"It *is* wonderful!" Phil shouted. "Uncle Eric is going to have all the business he can handle!"

After explaining to Denny about Mr. Swanson's decision, Phil said, "Let's tell Uncle Eric!"

"We can't," said Denny. "He's gone."

"Where?"

"To Webster Hollow—about ten minutes ago."

"Why?" yelled Phil.

"To sell the station," Denny muttered.

"We've got to stop him!" Phil cried.

Both boys knew that no telephone service was available. Not enough people lived out this way to make it worth while for the telephone company to put up a line. Suddenly Phil thought of the mobile telephone in Mr. Swanson's blue convertible and told Denny about it. "Where did Uncle Eric plan to go in Webster Hollow?" Phil demanded.

"He said he was going to leave the car at the McRae Garage. He's taking the one-fifteen train to Central City to see the man who wants to buy this property. He won't be back till noon tomorrow."

"If Mr. Swanson comes back soon," Phil said, "we can call the garage." He walked out across the crunching gravel and stared up the road. At last he saw the convertible approaching.

Both boys dashed breathlessly to the car. Phil managed to explain why he had to get word to his uncle. "Denny and I hope you'll let us use your mobile telephone to call him," Phil added. "We might catch him at the garage in Webster Hollow before he leaves for the city."

Mr. Swanson shook his head. "I'm almost sure it's no use," he said gravely. "I think I'm too far away from the mobile service station for it to get my signals. But let's try."

As the boys watched closely, he turned a control switch to the position marked "On," and a light appeared on the panel. Taking the telephone out of its holder, Mr. Swanson pointed to a push button  in the middle of the handset. "I press this button," he said, "to signal the operator at the mobile station. Then I release it when I want to listen."

The boys waited impatiently as he pressed and released the button several times. Finally he put the telephone back in its holder. "I'm sorry, boys. My signals are not answered." Then he suggested, "If you boys want to drive to Webster Hollow with me, you can keep trying to get the operator on the way."

Denny said, "You go, Phil. I'd better stay here and keep the gas station open."

"O.K.," said Phil as he opened the car door and slid in. "I'll be back just as soon as I can—with Uncle Eric, I hope!"

Mr. Swanson drove off. Every few minutes Phil took the telephone from its holder and pressed the little button on the handle. But nothing happened. No connection with the station operator was made. Between tries the boy watched the dashboard clock as minute after minute elapsed.

When the clock's hands indicated five minutes to one, Phil was close to desperation. He knew that it was now or never. If he did not get the mobile operator this time, Uncle Eric would surely have left the garage to catch his train. There would be no way to reach him in Central City, and Phil did not even know the name of the man who wanted to purchase the property.

Again Phil tried. This time the mobile service operator answered. Quickly Phil told her that he was calling Mr. Eric Lane at the McRae Garage in Webster Hollow. He waited a long moment.

Finally the operator said, "Your party has just left the McRae Garage."

Phil dropped the telephone back in its holder.

"Too late?" asked Mr. Swanson.

The boy nodded, almost sick with disappointment. For a moment he was tempted to give up the idea of trying to stop his uncle. But something kept him trying to figure out a way to do it. Of course! The railroad station!

Again Phil lifted the telephone and signaled the mobile service operator. "Please get the railroad station in Webster Hollow," he said, "and ask for Mr. Lane."

"One moment, please," requested the operator.

Anxiously Phil waited, hardly aware that the blue convertible had stopped beside the road. He kept the handset close to his ear and his eyes fastened on the minute hand of the dashboard clock.

Finally the boy heard an astonished voice saying, "This is Eric Lane."

"Uncle Eric! It's Phil! Don't sell your land!"

"Why not, boy?" asked Mr. Lane, his voice even more astonished. "I——" He paused as Phil tried to explain.

"I'm still mystified as to what this is all about," Mr. Lane said finally. "But I'll go on back to the garage and get my car."

"I'll meet you there," Phil shouted, "and tell you the whole story." With a grin of sheer delight, the boy replaced the handset.

Mr. Swanson started the car. Soon they were at the garage, where Mr. Lane eagerly awaited them. Forty minutes later Phil and his uncle were back at the gas station.

"Here's Uncle Eric," Phil yelled as Denny ran up to the car, "thanks to that mobile telephone!"

Mr. Lane chuckled. "And thanks to that fancy telephone you boys needn't worry any more about your school expenses. You'll always have summer jobs now."

Signals for Safety

For over a hundred years freight and passenger trains have gone highballing along over miles and miles of railroad track. The term "highballing" itself goes back to the earliest days of railroading, before the invention of electric lights. Then, as now, signals were needed, and the first ones used were two large balls. Each of these was attached by pulleys to a high post with a crossbar.

A black ball that was hung halfway up the post meant "Stop." A white ball hung high up near the  crossbar meant "Clear track. Go ahead." This "highball" signal told the engineer that he could go at full speed.

Flags were also used as early train signals, red for stop, white for go. Next came the semaphore, which is still used today. Signals by hand, lantern, and whistle were devised. Many of these, too, are still in use.

A station attendant, by holding his nose, tells a brakeman that he has an ungreased wheel bearing, or hot box. That could mean a wreck. A lantern swung across the track tells the engineer to stop. One held straight out at arm's length says "Slow down." If a conductor raises and then lowers a lantern or a flashlight, the engineer can go ahead.

Whistles, also, speak a language all their own. For example, if an engineer gives two long blasts, then one short and one long, he is saying, "We're approaching a grade crossing."

Later, the telegraph proved a great help to railroad safety. Information and warnings could be telegraphed from one signal tower to another.

But all these signals were only as reliable as the men who operated them. Today, automatic signaling devices are largely used. These ensure to a far greater degree the safety of the train, its crew, and the passengers.

Probably the most important of these devices is the Automatic Block System. This is used on all major railroads. It is operated by electric current flowing through the rails.

The track is divided into sections, or "blocks," with a signal light at the beginning of each block. The blocks vary in length. In long open stretches the block signals may be three to five miles apart. In the mountains, where the engineer cannot see so far ahead, they may be one mile apart. And in the dense traffic of terminal areas, they may be only one hundred fifty yards apart. As a train passes over the rails of one block, the lights behind and ahead of it automatically change color. The engineer sees a green or a yellow or a red light as his train approaches the block signal.

A green light indicates a clear track ahead.

The instant the engine of a train passes a green light, this green light turns red as a danger signal to any train that may be following.

This first light stays red till the caboose or the last coach of the train passes the next block signal. Then the first light changes to yellow, which is a caution signal.

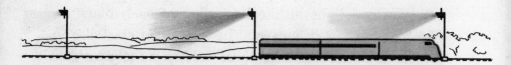

When the entire train has passed a third block signal, the first light changes to green or remains dark until another oncoming train causes the signal system to light up again.

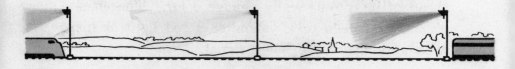

Thus an engineer gets the "green eye" only if the two blocks ahead are unoccupied. If a light is yellow, he slows down. If it is red, he STOPS!

Let us suppose that we are riding in the cab of the Diesel-powered Chicago-bound train No. 308 as it speeds through the night. The passengers are all asleep in their berths, confident that they will arrive safely at their destination.

James Dikeman, the engineer, sits about nine feet above the tracks on the right side of the cab. His left hand is on the throttle; his right hand controls the air-brake valve. One foot is on the "dead-man control." If he should faint and fall, his foot would slip off this pedal. Immediately the power of the Diesel would be shut off and the air brakes go on automatically.

On the left side of the cab, Albert Hooker, the fireman, watches the track ahead. The Diesel engines fill the cab with a rhythmic throbbing. Since these engines burn oil, Hooker does not have to shovel coal for them as he would have had to do on a steam locomotive. His job is to observe signals, watch dials and instruments in the cab, and keep aware of train orders to the engineer.

The engine's headlight illuminates the track for several hundred yards. The train is going ahead at full speed, for the block lights along the track are green mile after mile.

All during the trip Dikeman and Hooker call the signals back and forth to make sure that they are not missing a single danger warning.

Tonight, when No. 308 enters the Illinois River valley, it runs into a thick fog that grows denser as the train speeds forward. Soon the wayside block lights are totally invisible until the train is almost alongside them.

But Dikeman is not alarmed. Inside the cab is a panel on which these block signals also appear. Thus not even a thick fog or a blinding snowstorm can prevent the engineer from knowing whether or not the block ahead is clear. Now the green lights on the panel are glowing steadily. Dikeman keeps the throttle open and highballs down the track.

Suddenly the green glow of the cab signal lights changes to yellow. Instantly the engineer shifts the throttle several notches and applies the air-brake control lightly. The speedometer needle on the cab's instrument panel drops slowly.

"What's up?" asks Hooker, more to himself than to Dikeman. "That freight up ahead shouldn't be this close to us."

The train up ahead is a fast refrigerated freight. It is bound for Chicago laden with California fruits and vegetables.

Now the cab block signal shifts to red.

"Hold on, man!" warns Dikeman as he shuts off the power and applies the brakes, hard this time.

Brakes screech. The heavy roar of the Diesel units gradually drops to a soft purr. Just before 308 comes to a stop, a flickering red light appears dead ahead through the fog. This light, Dikeman and Hooker know, is a fusee, or flare, placed on the track bed by a brakeman of the stalled freight. And this fusee, they know, means "Stop."

A ghostly figure emerges from the mist and runs toward 308. Dikeman leans out. "What's up?" he calls.

"We hit a stalled truck at the grade crossing," explains the freight brakeman. "It's caught on the front of the engine."

"Anybody hurt?" asks Dikeman.

"No, the driver of the truck jumped in time," the brakeman replies.

"How long will we be here?" Hooker asks.

"We hit the truck about fifteen minutes ago. The freight is radio-equipped. So we called the traffic-control tower at Joliet. The dispatcher there said he'd have a wrecker sent out right away. Maybe it's come already. I'll find out."

Then Dikeman and Hooker see that the brakeman carries a short-wave radio in a case on his back.

"Jason, our fireman, has a walkie-talkie just like this up at the front end," says the brakeman as he lifts the microphone to his mouth and starts calling.

"Jason, this is Bill. Can you hear me?"

The brakeman is obliged to call several times before the fireman in the freight engine about a mile away replies. Bill listens and then grins. "Jason can see the big hook coming down the track now," the brakeman announces. "We'll soon be highballing again. I'd better get back."

He jogs down to his train. Not long afterwards the freight rumbles off to the nearest town, Ottawa. As No. 308 follows the freight train, Dikeman and Hooker discuss the accident.

"That radio-telephone saves lots of leg work and lots of time," Hooker concludes. "In the old days we might have been stalled there for hours while the brakeman hiked to the nearest town to get a wrecking crew out. How did we ever get along without two-way radio?"

"It's a big help all right," replied Dikeman.

At Ottawa the refrigerated freight pulls at once onto a siding, and No. 308 hurries past it. Hooker, glancing at the Diesel's signal panel, notes, "It's green ahead now. We won't pull into Chicago too much behind schedule after all."

Both men are grateful for the work of the dispatcher in the Joliet Traffic Control office. There the movements of all trains within a fifty-mile area can be followed by the dispatcher on a long board above his desk. This board is dotted with electric lights above rows of small levers.

When the wheels of a car travel over the rails, a system of wires carries electric messages to the dispatcher's control board. Lights on the board had told the dispatcher exactly where the refrigerated freight stopped. When it started up again, the dispatcher knew that also. As the freight neared Ottawa, he moved certain levers on his control board. Miles away signals were set and switches were thrown to guide the freight onto a siding at Ottawa. This enabled the passenger train to pass safely and continue its run.

Later, as No. 308 approaches the busy Chicago terminal area, the dispatcher in the control tower there keeps the main track clear for it by shifting other trains from one track to another. He does this merely by moving small levers. These automatically control the signal lights and switches that will fix the route No. 308 must take. Once these lights and switches are set, it is impossible for the tower "traffic policeman," or anyone else, to change them until the tracks are clear. This system of directing the movement of trains by remote control is known as "centralized traffic control."

Safely, and only a few minutes behind schedule, the sleek Diesel train threads its way through the maze of tracks and enters the station. In front of the bumping block at the track's end, it comes to a full stop.

Dikeman looks at the fireman and grins. Hooker grins back and gives the usual railroad man's sign for "The job's done; time to eat"—both thumbs up and fingers closed.

Song of the Train

Clickety-clack,
Wheels on the track,
This is the way
They begin the attack:
Click-ety-clack,
Click-ety-clack,
Click-ety, *clack*-ety,
Click-ety
Clack.

Clickety-clack,
Over the crack,
Faster and faster
The song of the track:
Clickety-clack,
Clickety-clack,
Clickety, clackety,
Clackety
Clack.

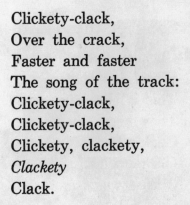

Riding in front,
Riding in back,
Everyone hears
The song of the track:
Clickety-clack,
Clickety-clack,
Clickety, *clickety*,
Clackety
Clack.

Expert Shovelman

"I'd give a lot to get on that shovel!" Dale Elgin exclaimed. "It's a marvelous machine!"

Carl Miller hitched his father's lunch pail higher on his arm and stared at his companion, who had recently moved to Carl's neighborhood.

"There's really nothing so marvelous about it," Carl said scornfully. "I've watched it stripping out coal for weeks. In fact, I can *run* it. I can make that fifteen-yard shovel move around like a spoon in a sugar bowl."

As the boys talked, they stepped off the path and started walking toward the cut to get a better view of the shovel. Carl failed to notice that they had gone past the warning flags into the danger zone.

"Quit bragging," laughed Dale. "It would take an expert to operate such a tremendous machine."

"I've been watching an
expert!" Carl retorted. "My
dad runs that shovel every
day. I've watched him work
in the shovel cab so often that I know what every
single lever is for. I've never really run the shovel
myself," he admitted, "but I know I could."

Carl pointed down at the machine. "There's my
dad in the cab now," he told Dale proudly. "The
man outside is his helper, Mr. Holland."

Just then Mr. Miller came rushing out of the cab
to the catwalk and waved the boys back. "Say!"
cried Dale. "Your dad seems angry."

With sudden dismay Carl realized that he had
led his friend dangerously close to the rim of the
steep cut that exposed a broad seam of coal.

"Get back!" Carl yelled. He grabbed frantically for Dale's sleeve but missed it.

The ground under them moved slightly. With a sharp cry Carl leaped backward, stumbled in the weeds, and fell. Tossing aside the lunch pail, he scrambled to his feet and turned to help Dale.

Then, speechless with horror, Carl saw that a wide crack had appeared in the sod between Dale and him. The edge of the cliff had split apart from the main body of land. Dale was crouching on the separated section, clutching at some weeds.

Straightening up suddenly, Dale was about to leap across the gap. But at that instant the ground quivered again. The separated section broke away and fell down into the cut, carrying Dale with it.

Terrified, Carl raced along the field parallel to the cut. A few hundred feet away, he came to the front end of the stripping operation. There the cut was shallow, almost on a level with the field. He slid quickly down into the cut and ran back toward the spot where Dale had fallen.

Carl found his friend sitting up and shaking his head in a dazed manner. By a miracle Dale had been thrown onto a pile of soft dirt. "You mean you're really not hurt?" Carl cried.

"Not much," Dale answered. Then suddenly he pointed to a nearby mound of dirt and rocks built up by the cave-in. "But look there!"

Carl clenched his teeth to keep from screaming as he stared horrified at the spectacle before him. At the foot of the landslide lay his father and Mr. Holland, face down and almost covered by dirt. A big flat section of rock from the slide was balanced dangerously over their bodies. Evidently the two men had rushed to aid Dale when he fell, and they themselves had been caught in the slide.

"We've got to do something!" Dale yelled, starting toward the men.

"Stop!" cried Carl shrilly. "Don't get too close to that mound or the rock may topple down on Dad and Mr. Holland. Stand back! Let me think!"

Although momentarily confused by shock, Carl soon realized that the men were either stunned by flying rocks or—— The boy shivered at the more terrifying possibility. The men must be freed immediately. But how? A single wrong move could bring that big rock crashing down on them.

Carl started to run for help. Then he stopped short, eying the stripping shovel. His skin began to prickle with excitement. An idea had suddenly occurred to him.

Dale, who was watching Carl closely, sensed the rash plan that his friend had in mind. "Do you— can you really run it?" he asked fearfully.

"Yes, I can!" The sound of his own determined voice gave Carl additional courage. Purposefully he headed for the shovel. After hurrying up the steel ladder that led to the catwalk, he darted into the cab.

The motor was still idling. The vibrating of the heavy floor seemed to indicate the steel monster's impatience to roar again into violent activity. Carl concentrated on the levers for a moment. Then he stepped out to the catwalk and called to Dale.

"Watch the dipper," he ordered. "I'm going to lower it and slip the teeth under the rock. Signal as soon as the teeth are hooked tightly under the edge. Then I'll lift up the rock. When I do, you drag Dad and Mr. Holland out from under it."

Back in the cab, Carl speeded up the motor. Its first roaring surge made him jump nervously. The big shovel seemed about to burst from under him. But he remembered that the machine was equipped with a device called a "governor" that controlled the motor's speed. If he operated the big machine properly, the dipper would not move any farther than he wanted it to.

For a few moments Carl just made the cables run through the pulleys. They stopped and started at the slightest touch of a lever. Then with great care he started to lower the dipper. Dale watched breathlessly as inch by inch the dipper came closer to the perilous big rock.

When the dipper was low enough, Carl turned it
to a down position in order to slip the teeth under
the rock. At last Dale signaled that the teeth were
securely caught under the edge. Carl eased the
clutch lightly. The pulleys whirred and the cable
grew taut. Slowly the stone was being lifted!

Then Dale's excited voice could be heard above
the noise of the motor. "Hold it! Hold it!"

Carl kept his hand firmly on the lever for fear
that the slightest movement would cause the teeth
to slip off the edge of the big stone. With his eyes
glued on the taut cable, he held his breath.

What was Dale doing? What took him so long?
The passing seconds seemed like hours.

"They're out!" Dale yelled from below. "Come
down!"

But Carl felt much too weak to move a muscle.
Trembling with relief, he sat with his hand still on
the control lever.

In a few moments he heard somebody mounting
the ladder. There was the sound of heavy shoes
coming along the catwalk. Then a strong, steady
hand reached out from behind him and gripped the
lever he was holding. Half dazed, the boy looked
up into his father's face close beside his own.

"Dad, you're all right! Is——" Carl could not
finish. He just watched as his father swung the
boom and dipper away from the landslide. There

was the click of a switch and a sudden silence as the motor stopped.

"I'm fine now, Son," said Mr. Miller. "So is Bill Holland. The fall knocked us out at first. I came to just before the dipper grabbed that rock. When I realized you were working the shovel, I was really scared. But you did a good job. To be an expert shovelman, though, you'll have to be more on the alert for danger than you were today."

"I've learned that now," Carl replied shakily.

"Well, come on down," said his father. "Dale and Bill Holland want to see you. Dale thinks that you're an expert shovelman already."

Carl flashed an understanding grin at his father and clattered down the steel ladder behind him.

Aeroplane

There's a humming in the sky,
There's a shining in the sky,
Silver wings are flashing by,
Silver wings are shining by.
Aeroplane,
Aeroplane,
Flying—high.

Silver wings are shining
As it goes gliding by.
First it zooms
And it booms;
Then it buzzes in the sky.

Then its song is just a drumming,
A soft little humming,
Strumming,
Strumming.

The wings are very little things;
The silver shine is gone.
Just a little black speck
Away down the sky,
With a soft little strumming
And a faraway humming.
Aeroplane,
Aeroplane,
Gone—by.

Crop Duster

The crop duster brought down his biplane on a makeshift airstrip near a small southwestern town. Wearily he hauled himself up from the cockpit and hopped to the ground. When he took off his goggles, the lower part of his face was a weird mask of chemical dust.

His two brothers rushed up to meet him.

"How did it go this evening, Cliff?" asked one of the younger boys.

"It's really murder out there," Cliff replied, his voice pitched above the chugging of the plane's idling engine. "No breeze. The dust mushrooms out everywhere. Sometimes I couldn't see even fifty feet ahead of me. And when I headed west, I was flying straight into the sun. This is the kind of day that crop dusters hate!"

Cliff and his brothers set about reloading with insect-killing powder for another dusting flight. Cliff stood on a wing while the other two passed sack after sack of dust up to him. These Cliff dumped into the roomy hopper, forward of the cockpit.

As soon as the hopper was loaded, Cliff climbed back into the cockpit, gunned his engine, and took off. The powerful engine pulled him up in a steep climbing bank, and he headed for the lettuce field he was to dust. As Cliff cruised over the field, he scouted it from a couple of hundred feet of altitude. Soon he was banking back in over one end of the field. He dropped quickly toward a high, menacing row of cottonwood trees forming the lettuce field's eastern boundary.

Cliff came in over the cottonwood trees so close that his wheels almost scraped the highest boughs. Then he plunged toward the ground as though he had lost control of the plane.

Finally, scarcely two feet above the ground, he leveled off. Turning on the dust blower, he began his dusting pass over the field.

Two thick jets of dust spurted back from beneath the fuselage as Cliff swept the length of the field, skimming low over the lettuce tops. Air currents churned up by his speeding plane sent the dust billowing across the field. There it lay heavy and still, like a thick fog.

Now it was clear what Cliff had meant when he said that it was "murder out there." Because of the low-lying dust, visibility was almost zero.

Next the crop duster approached a long row of cottonwoods that hemmed in the opposite end of the field. Soon he was so close that it would require a sharp pull-up to hurdle the trees. Cliff waited, however, until it seemed that he must surely smash into them. Then, with a roar, he arched into an almost vertical climb. The plane squeaked over the branches with only inches to spare.

Again and again the performance was repeated. A looping turn off one end of the field! Back down over the trees! Sweep low over the field! Then a roaring climb over the trees at the other end!

These almost incredible feats were not done to show off the crop duster's skill. Cliff was merely giving the farmer his money's worth. By waiting till the last possible instant before pulling up over the trees, Cliff was trying to make sure that the precious plant-saving dust was put on the farthest edges of the field.

But the crowning spectacle still remained. Cliff
finished a dusting pass down the length of the field
and then swung over to one side. Here there was
a barrier as forbidding as the row of cottonwood
trees—some high-voltage wires.

Cliff had decided to make a cross-field pass now
to put dust into spots that he had missed before.
Swinging down, he headed toward the power lines.
The plane vanished into a thick fog of dust. Then
it suddenly appeared again—flying *under* the power
lines, not over them!

When Cliff returned to the airport that was home base for his dusting company, it was hard to tell where the dust on his face left off and his sandy hair began.

"How was the job today?" asked someone at the airport.

"Just routine," Cliff replied matter-of-factly. He wiped some of the dust from his tanned face and added with a grin, "I think I must have pleased the customer today. I flew so low that if the man who owns that last field took a look, he'd probably find some of the green from his lettuce tops on my wheels."

"What about high lines?" Cliff was asked. "Did you have any trouble with them?"

"Not a bit," he answered, shaking his head. "I went under them nine times, with about three or four feet clearance top and bottom. I *can* take a plane through with six or eight inches of clearance. But the last time I did that, I caught my tail wheel on a fence wire and broke the wire. The farmer complained so much that I've been more careful ever since."

With another grin Cliff pulled off his helmet and stamped the dust off his clothes. After the plane was put away for the night, the flier could head for home. The day's wearisome and dangerous tasks were done.

Cliff, a former army pilot, is not unaware of the very real dangers of crop dusting. But he always insists that "a good pilot who knows his business is as safe as the equipment he has."

He adds, "I'd rather dust a field any day than drive cross-country in my automobile. After a pilot gets used to dusting, he flies almost automatically. True, a crop duster has to keep on his toes. He has to like the work. And he has to be a sharp chap who doesn't get tired and let his mind wander. If a pilot ever reaches the point where he thinks he's learned everything about dusting, it's time for him to retire. There isn't a dusting job I go out on that I don't learn something."

But whatever the job, there are perils other than power lines and tall trees. One big danger is the fact that the pilot carries no parachute. It would not be of much use to him if he did. He does his work too close to the ground to "hit the silk" if any trouble comes.

Fire is another danger. Some of the chemical mixtures, especially those containing sulphur, are highly combustible. They need only a spark to set them blazing.

Once a cloud of dust that Cliff was scattering on a field caught fire when he skimmed over a burning log. He managed to get away from the fiery dust, but only in the nick of time.

If a man is to succeed as a duster, he needs to know many things, and flying is only one of them. He must have some knowledge of insect life and of plant diseases.

He must also know how to keep his airplane and engine in good working condition. Frequently he has to be his own mechanic. Once after Cliff had had to make forced landings two days in a row, he worked on his plane engine around the clock, trying to get at the root of the trouble.

At first he thought that dampness in the air had caused the motor to overheat and miss. Then he suddenly had a hunch. Side by side on the ground he dumped quantities of two brands of gasoline— the one that he was using and another. He set a match to them. Cliff's brand burned black. The other brand burned clear. He had solved the mystery. Bad gasoline had caused the trouble.

One thing a crop duster soon learns is to pick a spot from the air where he can "sit down" quickly in case he has to make a forced landing. Another thing he soon learns is how to fly a straight row. He does this by selecting some object at the other end of the field—a tree, a bush, or a fence post— as a target.

But Cliff says that above all, a good crop duster needs to have a special brand of good luck riding with him all the time.

Shortly after dusting the lettuce field, Cliff had a narrow escape that made him feel more strongly than ever the importance of luck to a crop duster. This time he was dusting a field bounded on one side by a deep canal. The land itself was crossed with power lines.

Cliff was coming in over a power line, preparing to bank and turn to dust the field. Everything was going along as usual. Suddenly the plane's engine sputtered and then stalled completely. The crop duster tried frantically to get the engine working, but no answering roar greeted his efforts.

Below him were the high-voltage wires. And up ahead—not far away—was the canal. In the plane was a hopper full of highly combustible crop dust that would burst into flames if the plane crashed.

By only a few inches Cliff managed to miss the high-voltage wires. But in spite of all his efforts to start the engine, it would not respond. Quickly the pilot decided that he must make a forced landing. Even then he thought that the plane would probably roll into the canal, but he would have to take this chance.

Cliff braced himself for the shock of the landing. With a crash the plane hit the ground. It rolled bumpily across the field, heading directly for the water. Suddenly it bounced and tipped unsteadily to one side.

Bumping and circling crazily, the plane came at last to a full stop. It was at the very brink of the canal!

When Cliff pulled himself out of the cockpit, he discovered at once the miracle that had saved him. One of the landing wheels had collapsed. This had cut the speed of the roll and allowed the plane to ground-loop to a safe stop. Luck had really been riding with Cliff that time.

The duster's job is not limited to crop dusting. Cliff has often been called upon to fertilize fields from the air, to destroy weeds choking canals and irrigation ditches, or to fly over wide expanses of range land, scattering seed that will later provide grass for cattle herds.

One week he may be spraying cotton plants with a chemical that causes the leaves to drop off, thus preparing the way for a mechanical cotton picker. The next week he may be spraying a "stop-drop" chemical on orchards to make the fruit cling to the trees longer so that it will bring a better price when it is finally picked.

In winter when murderous frost threatens to destroy millions of dollars' worth of citrus fruits, the crop duster may be out in the dismal, cold hours before dawn, "freeze-proofing" the fruit. This he does by flying repeatedly back and forth over the citrus groves to keep the air circulating until the sun rises.

Up in the State of Washington the crop duster sprays apple orchards with a substance that kills a certain kind of bud that produces small apples. At the same time it preserves another kind of bud that produces large apples.

When Cliff recalls some of his operations in the Northwest, he says, "That brand of dusting is even riskier than the usual kind. Many of the farms and orchards in Washington spread across steep hillsides. The duster has to fly with one wing tip almost scraping the ground and the other one barely missing the side of a hill."

Cliff has also gone out on grasshopper-control missions. On those he has flown so low that the

grasshoppers bounced off his head. Frequently he has come back with the plane's struts and wires covered with the creatures.

Always the duster must be prepared to bound out of bed in the middle of the night to answer a call from a panic-stricken farmer. The man's land may have been invaded by a horde of insects, and he knows that the ravenous bugs can ruin his fields in twenty-four hours.

But Cliff takes such midnight calls for help in his stride, along with high-voltage wires, canals, and stalling engines. First of all, he likes what he is doing! Just as important, he realizes that his job is vital to his country's breadbaskets. Thanks to young men like Cliff, America is producing more food than ever before in its history.

Fun and Fancy

Falling Stars

One night in mid-August just before he went to bed, Eddie Blow stood on his grandmother's porch looking at the star-filled sky.

"Come on out and look, Grandma. There's a lot of shooting stars out tonight," he said.

"Make a wish, Eddie," his grandmother called to him from the kitchen.

"Aw, Grandma, that's superstition—wishing on falling stars. Falling stars are meteors. Chunks of matter that are flung off into space."

"Wait a minute, Eddie, till I turn off the water. I can't hear a thing," said his grandmother. In a little while she came out on the porch, wiping her hands on her apron. "Now what were you saying, Eddie?"

220

"I was saying, Grandma, that wishing on falling stars is—well, falling stars are great meteors or something. They shoot off like that, burning all the time. Sometimes they don't burn out altogether, and they fall to earth. Look, there's one now! What a beauty! It just went over the ridge back of the apple orchard."

"My, my!" said his grandmother. "That *was* a beauty. But I hope it did pass over the ridge and didn't fall to earth here. It would have come down just about on top of Grandfather's apple tree."

Grandfather's apple tree was the oldest tree in the orchard. It was called Grandfather's apple tree because it was said to be the first tree planted by Eddie's grandmother's grandfather. All the other trees in the orchard were said to be the children, grandchildren, and great-grandchildren of Grandfather's tree.

"I guess it went over the ridge all right," Eddie said. "But I wish a falling star would come down around here somewhere." Then he added hastily, "Just a little one, Grandma, one that wouldn't hurt anything."

"Well, none of them will be coming down just by wishing them down," said his grandmother. "And it's getting late, Eddie boy. You'd better get off to bed. If that big star or meteor or whatever it is did come down, I just hope it didn't come down on

Grandfather's tree. I'd like you to go up to the orchard the first thing tomorrow morning. I'm a little bit worried about Grandfather's apple tree."

"All right, Grandma. Of course I'll go up to the orchard," said Eddie. "Don't worry about that old meteor. Goodnight, Grandma."

Eddie bounded up the stairs two at a time. He swung open the door of his room as if he wanted to tear it off its hinges, took a running jump, and plopped on top of his bed. Then he ripped off one of his shoes without undoing the laces and stopped and thought . . .

What if the meteor really had come down in the apple orchard?

What if it had come down on Grandfather's apple tree?

What if it were up there right now, burning and burning? What did it look like, burning like that?

Eddie Blow was an eleven-and-a-half-year-old boy who was interested in science and nature. Eddie read books about science and nature in the library, and in his family's apartment in New York he had collections of animals, shells, insects, birds' eggs, and many other things. Every summer his mother sent him to visit his grandmother at her farm not far from Albany. In the country he did not need a collection of animals. He could see birds, animals, and insects in their natural surroundings.

Eddie helped around his grandmother's farm as much as possible. He went on errands and almost always did anything he was asked to do. His first job tomorrow was to go up to the apple orchard for Grandma.

"But why wait till morning?" he suddenly asked himself. "If that old meteor landed, I bet it's burning right now. Maybe I ought to go up tonight."

He heard his grandmother's bedroom door close.

Eddie thought another moment or two. Then he quietly got his flashlight and slipped out of his bedroom window. He slid down the drain pipe and landed on the ground below with a soft thud.

The moon had risen, and the road up the hill to the apple orchard was well lighted. Little animals scuttled across Eddie's path as he walked quickly along the road.

As Eddie rounded the trunk of one of the sturdy children of Grandfather's apple tree, he got a clear view of the old tree. At first glance there seemed to be nothing unusual about it. Then he saw something that sent prickles up and down his spine.

On a stout branch of the old tree, about ten feet above the ground, something moved! It had looked like part of the tree, a leafless, strangely shaped, small branch attached to the stout branch. Then it moved! It was unmistakably the figure of a wee man about three feet tall!

The little man was standing on the branch. But he was not standing on the top side of it. He was standing on the bottom side of it! Head down! He seemed to be surveying the countryside through a tiny spyglass.

Suddenly he fell head first from the branch and landed with a bang on his head. But his fall had no effect on him at all, for he was up on his feet in an instant. As he stood up, he saw Eddie for the first time.

"Speak . . . English?" asked the little man in a high, squeaky voice.

"Y-y-yes, sir," stammered Eddie.

"Good," said the little man. "One minute. Must adjust nongravity shoes."

He squatted on the ground, twirling some knobs and screws on his heavy shoes. Then he got up and walked over to the trunk of Grandfather's apple tree. And he kept right on walking, straight up the side of the tree and back along the stout branch from which he had fallen.

"One minute," said the little man again. "Must record observations."

After a few moments of peeking through his little spyglass, he took what appeared to be a tiny typewriter out of one of his many pockets. He quickly tapped its keys a number of times. Then he put it back in his pocket and walked down the tree trunk to the ground and up to the astonished Eddie.

"You . . . are native?" he asked.

"What?" exclaimed Eddie.

"One minute," said the little man. Out of another pocket he pulled a small box and snapped it open. The box was filled with luminous cards. Selecting a card, he squinted at it and then spoke again.

"You . . . are born . . . in United States . . . of America?"

"Yes, sir," said Eddie.

"Good," said the little man. As he looked at his luminous cards again, Eddie began to get over the first shock of seeing him. "What's going on here?" Eddie said to himself. "Who is he to ask me a lot of questions in my grandmother's apple orchard?"

"Look here!" said Eddie loudly. "What's going on? Who do you think you are? You'd better——"

As Eddie spoke, the little man stopped looking through his cards and began to adjust a small knob on a bracelet that he wore on his wrist. And as Eddie's voice rose angrily, the little man touched the boy's chest lightly with one finger.

Eddie sat down hard on the ground!

"Speak slowly . . . no anger," said the little man.

Eddie scrambled to his feet, his fists clenched.

"I answer question," said the little man, pointing his finger menacingly. "I am Scientist-Explorer from Planet Martinea."

Eddie gasped. "G'wan, there's no such planet!"

The little man hastily studied his cards again.

"What means g'wan?" he asked.

"G'wan means—what difference does it make?" asked Eddie. "What's that box?"

"Dictionary box," said the little man. "Explains language. English language, Martinean language. Our Language Scientists study American English through high-powered telescopes from Martinea."

"How could they?" asked Eddie suspiciously.

"Your language on highways—'Go slow! Speed limit 40 miles! Turn left! Hot dogs!' Martinean Language Scientists construct language from these examples."

Eddie blinked. "Where's this Martinea?"

The little man pointed in the general direction of the moon. "Martinea outside your sun's path."

"Well, I never heard of it," said Eddie. "How did you get here?"

"Come, I show you," the little man said. Turning, he walked over the ridge behind Grandfather's apple tree. Eddie followed. About ten feet from the tree trunk, the little man stopped. Exercising surprising force, he began to pull away some old branches that filled a rather large gully.

In a few minutes Eddie could see something that looked like an immense overturned aluminum dish. There were strange gadgets on its metal surface, and a number of metal tubes along its outer rim.

"A Flying Saucer!" cried Eddie. "But how can it be? There are no Flying Saucers!"

Quickly the little man opened his dictionary box. "F . . . F . . . Frying Pan? Flying——" he muttered as he looked through the cards. "Flying Saucer not in dictionary. What is Flying Saucer?"

"A big professor said there are no such things as Flying Saucers," replied Eddie. "I read it in a scientific magazine in the library."

The little man took out his typewriter and tapped away at it for a second. "Professor correct—no Flying Saucers," he said. "This is Astral Rocket Disk. Perhaps you say Space Ship."

He covered up the metal ship and turned again to Eddie.

"Information, please," he said. "Where hotel? Must rest. Must wait for—how you say—this side earth revolve to sun."

"You mean until daylight," said Eddie.

"Yes, daylight," agreed the little man.

"There's no hotel around here," Eddie said. "If you want to rest tonight, come to my grandmother's house. She won't mind, I think. I have a chest in my room long enough for you to sleep on."

"Good," said the man. "Speed limit forty miles."

He adjusted some knobs on his shoes, set a little dial in the direction Eddie had pointed, and took off. Eddie found himself racing through the orchard after the little man, who moved with amazing speed toward Eddie's grandmother's house.

The next morning Eddie was not sure whether it was his grandmother's voice or the sun streaming into his window that woke him. As he lay there half awake, he said to himself, "Dreams are good things. A fellow can have more adventure with his eyes closed than he can when they're wide open. Dream about flying . . . dream about——"

Eddie yawned widely, stretched, and closed his eyes again. "Be down in a minute, Grandma," he mumbled sleepily as he fell back on the pillow.

After a few minutes his grandmother called again. "Eddie, remember your promise. You said you'd go up to the orchard for me this morning."

Eddie's eyes flashed open. That's what he had dreamed about, going to the orchard! He sat bolt upright in his bed as he remembered the little man. He jerked his head around and looked over at the chest where the little man had stretched out after they climbed up the drain pipe to Eddie's room.

There was no one on the chest! Quickly Eddie looked around his room. He could detect no sign of the little man.

"Whew!" said Eddie. "What a dream that was! But was it really a dream? After breakfast I'll go up to the orchard and see."

The Caliph's Clock

The Caliph Keeps Up with the Times

It was morning in the city of Chunder-abad-dad.
The Caliph sat upon his divan moodily stroking his
beard. Suddenly he called impatiently, "Selim!
Are you never going to eat breakfast?"

As he spoke, he cracked and emptied into his cup
the last of the soft-boiled eggs.

The Grand Vizir laid down the morning paper
he had been reading. "Oh," said he, "how could I
know it was breakfast time? You didn't ring a bell."

"You could look at the hourglass."

"It leaks," replied the Vizir. "Somebody cracked
it—not I."

"Why did you not observe the sundial?" said the
Caliph stiffly.

"There is a dark cloud over the sun. Why don't you have a sundial that works in cloudy weather?"

"Cloudy weather!" exclaimed the Caliph. "This is not cloudy weather!"

"It is for me," said the Grand Vizir ruefully, and sank back into gloom.

As the Caliph of Chunder-abad-dad finished eating, a wandering Yankee peddler knocked at the palace door. The Grand Vizir immediately rose when the peddler entered.

He wore a pinch-backed coat, a bright green hat, and white spatterdashes, and he had an air of boastful superiority. He very briskly said that he had clocks to sell.

"Clocks?" asked the Caliph, curious. "Clocks? Let's see them."

The peddler produced a timepiece. "This clock has chimes and a cuckoo," he said cheerfully.

He slipped his hand inside the clock and twisted something that made the insides cluck like a hen. The clock began to go faster. The peddler smiled.

"This," said he, "is a wonderful clock for communities that wish to keep up with the times."

"And will it inspire idle people to employ their wasted hours?"

"Adopt our daylight-saving plan, and there will be no wasted hours."

"A daylight-saving plan!" exclaimed the Caliph. "Will this clock save daylight?"

"Sire," said the peddler, "this clock will save daylight as a miser saves pennies. Our daylight-saving attachment usually sells at ten *dinars*. We can make it six *dinars* to you. Shall I say 'Sold'?"

The Caliph hesitated.

The peddler waved his hands. "This unparalleled timepiece runs forty days and forty nights with but a single winding," said he. "It also has a musical attachment that can play twelve perfectly ripping tunes. The cuckoo *cucks* on the hour and *koos* on the half-hour. With every daylight-saving device we give a thousand circulars praising the merits of daylight saving as conducted by our clock."

"I want it," said the Caliph.

"To install the daylight-saving device is marvelously easy," said the peddler. "Just set your sundials by the clock, go to bed, and forget it. When you wake in the morning, you'll be surprised to see what time it is."

"I often am!" said the Grand Vizir.

"I must have it," said the Caliph, and forthwith purchased the clock from the peddler for the price that he had asked.

"We shall begin at once to save daylight!" said the Caliph. "We shall now keep up with the times. Go! Set all the sundials in the town to keep time with my clock."

Then he caused the clock to be set upon a marble column in the middle of the courtyard and published a proclamation throughout the city, saying:

"I am the Caliph of Chunder-abad-dad, and I have established a Clock. The time of it is *my* time; the hours of it are the right time; its hours are those of the Faithful. From now on there shall be no other time in the city of Chunder-abad-dad."

"Now, wind it up!" he said.

The official clock-winder inserted the key and wound the Caliph's clock. It started with a double chime and such a strange and threatening whir in its insides that the clock-winder ducked.

The pendulum began to vibrate with an alert, sharp sound, with a clattering of the levers and a brisk, hurrying ring of a silvery bell. The minute hand started its steady round. The hour hand began its pompous revolution. The second hand danced and capered like a mosquito. The fateful clock was going.

"From now on," said the Caliph, "there shall be no other time in the city of Chunder-abad-dad!"

Watchmen went about the streets everywhere, crying, "Set your sundials! Set your sundials by the Caliph's clock! Who wastes his hours throws away the golden gift of Allah! Set your sundials."

Confusion Reigns in Chunder-abad-dad

The Caliph and the Vizir sat for hours, watching the pendulum swing.

"Plague take the thing!" muttered the Vizir. "It has an evil look and sounds like a hen in the rain!" The clock was running with a threatening whir that never ceased nor changed, but seemed hourly to go faster and faster.

"How fast the time flies!" he said nervously.

"Yes," replied the Caliph, "the days are so long at this season that time has to fly fast to get through."

"And the morning is oddly short, Sire. See, it is already half-past ten!"

"Oh, that is the daylight-saving device," said the Caliph carelessly. "It is saving part of the day. By thus using less in the morning, we shall have more in the afternoon. It is indeed clever."

The day passed, and evening came gently up the east.

The Caliph sat by his window. There was a bewildered look on his face. He held an almanac in his hand, and he had one eye on the clock.

"Selim," he said uneasily, peering out the window. "It is high time it should be dusk. Sunset was due at ten minutes past six by the almanac. It is more than an hour behind time. I wish you would go out and attend to it."

"But, Your Highness," said the Vizir, "it cannot be sunset until the sun *sets*."

"What?" cried the Caliph. "Must I wait for the sun? Am I not the Caliph? Is it not mine to say what the hours shall be in Chunder-abad-dad?"

"Surely!" replied the Vizir. "But, Your Highness, does not the sun *set* at sunset? And is it not sunset when the sun *sets*? How can it then be sunset until the sun *does* set? We have but one sun, and only when it *sets* is it sunset!"

The Caliph looked dazed. "By the prophet's beard, Selim!" he said. "You can say less in more words than anyone I have ever heard. Let the sun set when it will. I will attend to the sunset. When my clock says, 'This is sunset,' it *shall* be sunset. This clock is *my* clock. Its hours are the *right* hours. There shall be no other time whatever in the city of Chunder-abad-dad!"

He tossed the hourglass out of the window. It fell with a crash in the street.

"Go," he said. "Send all the people to bed. It is high time they retired."

Being well acquainted with the Caliph, everybody made haste to go to bed.

Sometime in the night the Vizir woke, and being very thirsty, went out to the hydrant in the courtyard to get himself a drink. In the hush that was over the city he could hear the splash of fountains, and in the palace courtyard the Caliph's clock was running with a strange, uneasy sound.

It had been running fast at sunset. It was running faster now. It sounded as if it were running a race with itself and were gaining on every round. He could hear it catch step and break again at every dozen ticks.

It struck twice as he stood in the courtyard.

It struck thrice as he crept into bed.

It struck four times as he fell asleep.

And while all the world was as black as your hat, he heard the Caliph cry, "Breakfast!"

It was intensely dark. The chill of night was in the air, and the stars were still in the sky.

"Breakfast!" gasped the Vizir as he sat up in his bed. "Why, we have just had supper!"

"The clock says it is breakfast time!" said the Caliph. "Come promptly, or I'll know the reason why."

"I cannot eat a mouthful!" protested the Vizir.

"You'd better!" growled the Caliph. "If you slight the buckwheat cakes, we'll have an account to settle."

The Vizir ate a large breakfast. In fact, he ate too much.

As he finished his oatmeal, the clock struck nine. As he ate his buckwheats, the clock struck ten. As he drank his coffee, it struck again.

"Go!" cried the Caliph. "Drive the beasts out to pasture before the morning is spent!"

The Vizir looked at the Caliph's eye. It was as red as a ruby. He hurried out to the stables, woke the sheep, aroused the goats, and drove the cows to pasture. He ran back through the darkness and tottered up the palace steps just as the sun rose.

The Caliph was eating gloomily. "Are you aware that it is now dinnertime?"

"Dinnertime?" stammered the Vizir.

"It is twelve o'clock!" cried the Caliph. "It is high noon by the clock."

"But it is not high noon by the noon-mark on the stones in the palace yard. The sun is this minute rising!" replied the Vizir hastily.

"Don't argue with me," said the Caliph.

"I was not arguing with you. I was just stating a fact. Stating a fact is not argument."

"Then why do you always cross me?" said the Caliph sourly. "When the clock strikes twelve,

237

and I say it is twelve, why do you contradict me?
See, the clock says it is twilight! You'd better go
put up the stock."

The Vizir chased the cows home, shut up the
herds, folded the flocks, hustled the fowls into the
henhouse, shook down straw for the donkeys and
camels, gave the elephants hay, and came sheepishly
back to the palace.

"Someone is wasting a deal of daylight," he said
to nobody in particular as he eyed the rising day.

"Wasting daylight?" cried the Caliph. "How
can one be wasting daylight who is not using it?
One cannot waste what he does not use. Nobody
is wasting daylight. We are saving quantities.
Day by day we are saving time. Hour by hour we
are gaining upon the sun. Soon we shall have
whole days to dispose of!"

And the clock went scuttling along.

Meantime in Chunder-abad-dad things were going very badly. The astonished populace rose in
haste and chased the hours with flying feet. They
chased them all day. Nobody knew just what time
it was; and, apparently, when they did, it wasn't,
which was confusing.

The sun said it still was Tuesday noon when the
clock said breakfast time the next Sunday morning.
Before twilight that day the Caliph and the Grand
Vizir had eaten two breakfasts, two luncheons, two

dinners, two suppers, and were preparing once more for breakfast. Thus, in extraordinary fashion, time sped by in Chunder-abad-dad.

Days and nights ran round like water beetles. Meals followed one another like drops of spattering rain. Hours fled by like the flying balls shot from a Roman candle.

Every hour it became more difficult to keep up with the Caliph's clock.

Worn out with constant hurry, the Caliph and all the people fell into a deep sleep. But the Grand Vizir in his anxiety lay as restless as a cat.

A Miracle Comes to Pass

The road from Samarcand ran down to Chunder-abad-dad like a wide ribbon wandering through the dusty plain. Down the road came a merchant on

a mule, bringing his wares to the city. When he
reached Chunder-abad-dad, he saw that its walls
were deserted. He listened, but all he heard was a
sound like a simoom in the distance. It was the
people of Chunder-abad-dad snoring together.

He pounded on the town gates and shouted, but
there came no reply. Opening the rear gate, he
rode in through the deserted streets.

Over the minarets the noonday sun streamed in
a flood of light. Yet all was still. Not a person
was to be seen; not so much as a dog stirred in an
alley. Cold fear crept over the merchant. "In the
name of King Solomon's ant!" he cried. "Have I
come to a city of the dead?"

The square before the palace lay empty in the
sunshine. There was not even a beggar asleep by
the gate, but he could hear the fountains splashing.

"In the name of Sheba's mule!" he cried. "Is
anyone living here?"

He heard a shutter open in the wall. He shaded
his eyes and squinted up through the sunshine.
He saw the head of the Vizir emerging through a
crevice.

"Hush!" said the Grand Vizir.

"What in the name of——"

"Hush! Hush, if you love your life!"

The merchant stared in amazement. "What has
touched your wits?" he gasped.

"On your honor, tell me, what time is it?" asked the Grand Vizir. "When I ask what time, I mean what hour by Allah's time."

"High noon," said the stranger, marveling much.

"Do you speak the truth?" cried the Vizir.

"Brother, if you cannot take my word for it, just look at the sun. My mule stands with his four feet on his shadow but once in the day."

"What is the day of the week?"

"Friday."

"Friday?" whispered the Vizir, his eyes popping. "See my gray hairs. I am an old man. Do not fool me, friend."

The puzzled merchant drew from his saddlebags the *Samarcand Gazette* and showed it to the Vizir.

"You may see the date for yourself."

"*Bismillah!*" gasped the Vizir hoarsely. "Friend, in this stupid city of Chunder-abad-dad it is forty-two minutes past twelve o'clock come next Sunday fortnight! We are now two weeks ahead of the sun. I knew there was something wrong with that clock, or it would not have kept a cuckoo!"

"Clock?" said the merchant.

"Clock," said the Vizir.

"Show me the thing," said the merchant.

With finger on lip, in tiptoed silence, the Grand Vizir led the merchant through the corridor into the court.

The Caliph's clock stood there upon the top of its marble column.

"There," said the Vizir bitterly, "is the machine that has made this city mad!"

At that moment the clock, which by traveling at breakneck speed had accomplished a six weeks' journey in four weeks' time, ran down.

The overtaxed mainspring relaxed with a whine. Something popped inside!——BING! it went—— z-z-z-z-z-z-z-z-z-ee-ee——SPANG——CHUCK!

With a tremendous whir-r-r, suddenly ended, the clock hands flew wildly round, once, twice, thrice. They gave one feeble wave, trembled, and stood still. The hands were just at twelve.

The official clock had stopped!

The two men stood aghast.

From his bedroom across the corridor came the Caliph's voice, "Selim! Selim!"

"Allah save you," gasped the merchant.

"Selim! Selim!" came the stern voice. "Answer me instantly. What are you doing? Have you dared to lay hands upon my royal clock?"

The Grand Vizir clung to a pillar. His legs refused to support him. "Al-Al-Allah!" was all that he could say.

But the merchant of Samarcand was equal to the emergency. "A miracle," he roared, and fell on his knees.

"Kneel!" he gasped to the Vizir. "Kneel, if
you value your neck! And shout, 'A miracle!'"

"A miracle! A miracle!" shouted the Vizir as
he dropped to his knees. "But I don't know what
it is."

"Bellow," whispered the merchant. "Louder and
louder." And they bellowed together.

The Caliph appeared in his doorway. There was
flaming wrath in his eyes. He stood for a second
speechless, candle in hand, staring at the spectacle
before him.

"A miracle!" bellowed the Grand Vizir.

"A miracle!" shouted the merchant.

"Where?" said the Caliph stormily. "And what is this miracle?"

"That a clock should cease running with its hands uplifted forever in praise at the hour of prayer!" cried the merchant.

"Cease running? My clock?" cried the Caliph. He threw a glance at the Vizir that made Selim's heart stop beating.

"Great is the Caliph! Our Caliph is mighty!" cried the merchant joyfully.

"In his hands he holds the hours as one gathers loose sand in a bowl. He commands the darkness to pass, and it passes. He says, 'The day comes,' and it comes. He gathers the daylight into a bag and presents the extra time to his people. *Allah hu akbar!* Our Caliph is mighty!"

The Caliph now began to feel as if he had done something out of the ordinary; as, indeed, he had. He assumed a few airs. He strutted and began to twist his mustache.

"Behold!" said the merchant. "While the mighty slept, Time came to a stop; the wheels of the Hours stood still. While the Caliph slept, the calendar caught up with the clock. Hail to the Controller of Calendars! The sun, moon, and stars are his servants. The seasons are his toys!"

The Caliph smiled modestly. He loved to hear mild praise of himself.

"Our Caliph," continued the merchant, "has laid up fourteen days in his treasury as a miser would lay up his pence. Through his wonderful genius the city of Chunder-abad-dad is a whole fortnight ahead of the sun! Great minds are always ahead of their time!

"And now behold," said the merchant, and waved at the clock. "This crafty machine confesses the truth: there is no time but Allah's."

"This is a very wise man," thought the Caliph. "A very wise man indeed." And he drew himself up pompously to his full height.

"Now," said the Caliph, "I have had enough of trying to keep up with the times. I shall never hurry again."

Then the Caliph sent forth a royal proclamation, saying:

"In the name of the Prophet! I, Sulieman the Magnificent, Caliph of Chunder-abad-dad, have now saved two weeks, which otherwise would have been wasted in sheer foolishness, and return them as a gift to my people that they may live them over; that those who did ill may do well; that those who did well may do better."

And if you ever should come to Chunder-abad-dad, you will find a city where everyone is idle and happy, doing just as he pleases; where no one ever hurries, yet the world goes very well.

Jonathan Bing

Poor old Jonathan Bing
Went out in his carriage to visit the King,
But everyone pointed and said, "Look at that!
Jonathan Bing has forgotten his hat!"
(He'd forgotten his hat!)

Poor old Jonathan Bing
Went home and put on a new hat for the King,
But up by the palace a soldier said, "Hi!
You can't see the King; you've forgotten your tie!"
(He'd forgotten his tie!)

Poor old Jonathan Bing,
He put on a *beautiful* tie for the King,
But when he arrived an Archbishop said, "Ho!
You can't come to court in pyjamas, you know!"

Poor old Jonathan Bing
Went home and addressed a short note to the King:

> If you please will excuse me
> I won't come to tea;
> For home's the best place for
> All people like me!

Rhyming Ink

Once there was a man called Simon Smug; his wife was called Sarah, and they kept a shop.

Every morning at eight o'clock precisely, Simon unbolted the shop door and took down the shutters. Then he stood behind the counter and weighed out sugar and currants and wrapped up parcels and made out bills and said, "What next can I get for you, ma'am?" and "Dreadful weather for the time of year!" to all the customers. And every evening as the clock struck seven, Simon put up the shutters again and fastened the door.

"Now I'm going to enjoy myself!" he would say, rubbing his hands with enthusiasm.

Sometimes he enjoyed himself by sitting with his feet inside the fender reading the paper to Sarah. Sometimes he enjoyed himself pottering about the back yard and painting the water barrel or sowing Virginian Stock seed in the rockery. Sometimes he enjoyed himself by falling asleep in his chair.

And then one day he decided to become a poet.

"You'd be surprised at the thoughts that come into my head, Sarah," said he. "I'm going to put them into poetry and become famous."

He got out a very large sheet of paper and a very large pen and a very large pot of ink and sat down at the kitchen table. Sarah looked at him proudly.

"Just fancy me a poet's wife!" she thought, and held her head two inches higher than usual.

Simon began to write as fast as he could. "Just listen to this and tell me if you ever heard so fine a beginning to a poem," cried he.

Some poets praise the hairy lion;
I praise the hippopotamus;

"And what comes next?" inquired Mrs. Smug.

"I don't know yet," said Simon. "I haven't had the time to find a rhyme."

He sat at the table and thought and thought and thought. He bit the end of his pen to shreds; he found a box of nibs and tried them all; he rumpled his hair and inked his face and made scribbles and patterns all round the edge of the paper; but it was no use.

"I don't believe there's a rhyme to hippopotamus in any language under the sun!" he groaned.

"Why not start with something easier?" suggested Mrs. Smug.

So Simon began again; he began a dozen poems at least, but he could not finish one.

"Is anything wrong, my dear?" asked Sarah.

"Wrong!" echoed Simon. "I should think there is! There's not a single rhyme to any word I've used. I can no more make poetry without rhymes than you can make pancakes without eggs! I'll never be a poet at this rate."

It was the same every time he sat down to write. His verses never got beyond the first two lines, and all for want of rhymes. He grew quite thin and ill-tempered with worry; he lost his appetite; he lost his sleep; he was impatient with the customers and made mistakes in their orders. Wherever he was and whatever he was doing, he was muttering scraps of poetry to himself and trying to find the words he wanted.

"Things can't go on like this," said Mrs. Smug, but she had not the least idea how to stop them. Then she saw the advertisement for Rhyming Ink.

Important to Poets!

Here is the Most Wonderful Invention of the Age. Just dip your pen in Rhyming Ink (only ten shillings a bottle) and you cannot help writing poetry. If our Ink fails to find a rhyme to any word in the dictionary, your money will be refunded.

"Now if that isn't exactly what Simon wants!" she cried, and sent for some rhyming ink immediately. She did not tell Simon anything about it, of course, for she felt sure he would not feel like a real poet if he knew his rhymes came out of a bottle instead of out of his head.

When the ink arrived, she washed the old inkpot that Simon always used and filled it to the brim. "Now perhaps we'll have a little peace," she said.

Presently Simon came in, gave a great sigh, and
sat down at the kitchen table to write poetry, just
as usual. He sighed again as he spread out a clean
sheet of paper; he sighed as he chose a clean nib for
his pen; he sighed as he opened the inkpot, for he
supposed that everything would happen as it had
always done before and that in five minutes he
would be rumpling his hair and rolling his eyes in
his struggle to find a rhyme. And he had thought
of such a beautiful beginning for a poem!

I would that in the summer sun
I flitted as a butterfly!

He wrote that much quite quickly, but that was not
surprising because he always wrote the first two
lines without any trouble; the surprising thing was
that the pen went on and finished the verse!

But then before the day was run
Perhaps I'd in the gutter lie!

"I've done it!" shouted Simon Smug. "I've done
it! I've written a poem!"

"There, now, just fancy that!" said Sarah.

"But I don't suppose I'll ever be able to write
another," he added gloomily.

"I should try if I were you," said Sarah.

"I might as well," said Simon. "I'll see if I can
finish the hippopotamus one."

He dipped his pen in the ink and began to write:

Some poets praise the hairy lion;
I praise the hippopotamus;

And once again the pen went gliding on:

He's got a mouth with teeth like iron--
If he should nip, oh! what a fuss!

"I've done it again!" he exclaimed. "I can write poetry as easily as signing my name!"

He scrawled *Simon Smug* across the paper, by way of illustration, and then gave a gasp, for under his name he had written *Oh, what a mug!*

"I've made a poem even of that," he said in astonishment, "only it's not a very good one. I'm a poet at last! I shall sit and write poetry all day long and never serve in the shop any more."

"You don't mean it, do you?" asked Mrs. Smug.

"Of course I do," said Simon. "Fancy wasting my time weighing out rice and tea and things like that when I've found out how clever I am. If anyone attends to the shop, it must be you, my dear, for I'm far too busy to do anything about it."

At first Mrs. Smug made the best of things, but it was inconvenient to have to keep dropping her dishcloth or potato peeler to wait on customers.

It was really very pleasant not to have Simon moaning and groaning over his rhymes, but after

a few days she wished she had never bought the rhyming ink.

The kitchen table was smothered in papers; poems fluttered to the ground with every opening of the door; they got into the washtub and the gravy and the flour barrel and the coal scuttle. And if, by chance, Sarah had a moment in which to sit down and rest, Simon would begin to read his favorite pieces to her. What with the worry of so much poetry in the kitchen and the worry of so little help in the shop, she began to feel quite worn out.

The trouble really came to a head when she used the rhyming ink herself. She would never have done it if she had had time to think, but the shop was so full of customers that she was quite flurried, and when she lost her pencil, she carried off the inkpot from under Simon's nose.

"But I can't write without ink!" protested Simon.

"Then you can spend the time tidying the kitchen," said Sarah over her shoulder. "It's disgraceful!"

She deftly wrote receipts and bills and orders, and then she took the ink back to her husband. But never once did she remember that the ink was not of the ordinary kind—until the customers returned, red-faced and angry.

"What do you mean by putting down *white mice* on my bill?" cried one. "I ordered a pound of rice, and you have charged for three white mice as well."

"And I ordered a pot of jam," said another, "and you've written underneath *To boil with ham!*"

"Just look at this receipt!" cried a third. "I never saw a bill receipted like this in my life!"

Received with thanks,
Dear Mrs. Banks,
One pound and four—
You owe me more—
A kiss and hug
From Sarah Smug!

"It's that rhyming ink!" cried poor Sarah. And she rushed into the kitchen.

"I've written another poem since you brought me the ink again," said Simon. "It begins, 'Behold the wriggling caterpillar——'"

"I don't care how it begins!" cried Mrs. Smug, and she seized the bottle and emptied the ink out of the window all over the rockery. "You just clear all those papers off the table and look after the shop as you used to do. I've had more than enough poetry, and that's the end of it!"

To tell the truth, Simon had had more than enough poetry, too, and was quite glad to be back behind the counter. But Sarah was wrong in thinking that emptying the bottle out of the window was the end of the matter. The Virginian Stocks began to behave in a most extraordinary way. Instead of being miserable and straggling, they grew and budded and blossomed just as though ink were their favorite fertilizer.

"What a charming back yard you have," exclaimed all Simon's visitors. "Your rockery is as pretty as a poem!"

Which just shows what rhyming ink can do—at least the kind at ten shillings a bottle.

The Story of Dr. Dolittle

Once upon a time, many years ago—when our grandfathers were little children—there was a doctor; and his name was Dolittle—John Dolittle, M.D. "M.D." means that he was a proper doctor and knew a whole lot.

He lived in a little town called Puddleby-on-the-Marsh. All the folks, young and old, knew him well by sight. And whenever he walked down the street in his high hat everyone would say, "There goes the Doctor! He's a clever man." And the dogs and the children would all run up and follow behind him; and even the crows that lived in the church tower would caw and nod their heads.

The house he lived in, on the edge of the town, was quite small; but his garden was very large and had a wide lawn and stone seats and weeping willows hanging over. His sister, Sarah Dolittle, was house-keeper for him; but the Doctor looked after the garden himself. He was very fond of animals and kept many kinds of pets. Besides goldfish in the pond at the bottom of his garden, he had rabbits in the pantry, white mice in his piano, a squirrel in the linen closet, and a hedgehog in the cellar. He had a cow with a calf, too, an old lame horse—twenty-five years of age—and chickens and pigeons and two lambs and many other animals. But his favorite pets were Dab-Dab the duck, Jip the dog, Gub-Gub the pig, Polynesia the parrot, and the owl, Too-Too.

His sister used to grumble about all these animals and said they made the house untidy. And one day when an old lady with rheumatism came to see the Doctor, she sat on the hedgehog, who was sleeping on the sofa, and never came to see him any more, but drove every Saturday to Oxenthorpe, another town ten miles off, to see a different doctor.

Then his sister, Sarah Dolittle, came to him and said, "John, how can you expect sick people to come and see you when you keep all these animals in the house? It's a fine doctor would have his parlor full of hedgehogs and mice! That's the fourth personage these animals have driven away. Squire Jenkins and the parson say they wouldn't come near your house again—no matter how sick they are. We are getting poorer every day. If you go on like this, none of the best people will have you for a doctor."

"But I like animals better than the best people," said the Doctor.

"You are ridiculous," said his sister, and walked out of the room.

So, as time went on, the Doctor got more and more animals; and the people who came to see him got less and less. Till at last he had no one left—except the Cat's-meat-Man, who didn't mind any kind of animals. But the Cat's-meat-Man wasn't very rich, and he only got sick once a year—at Christmas time, when he used to give the Doctor sixpence for a bottle of medicine. Sixpence a year wasn't enough to live on—even in those days, long ago; and if the Doctor hadn't had some money saved up in his money box, no one knows what would have happened.

And he kept on getting still more pets; and of course it cost a lot to feed them. And the money he had saved up grew littler and littler.

Then he sold his piano and let the mice live in a bureau drawer. But the money he got for that, too, began to go, so he sold the brown suit he wore on Sundays and went on becoming poorer and poorer.

And now, when he walked down the street in his high hat, people would say to one another, "There goes John Dolittle, M.D. There was a time when he was the best-known doctor in the West Country. Look at him now. He hasn't any money, and his stockings are full of holes!" But the dogs and the cats and the children still ran up and followed him through the town the same as when he was rich.

It happened one day that the Doctor was sitting in his kitchen talking with the Cat's-meat-Man, who had come to see him with a stomach ache. "Why don't you give up being a people's doctor and be an animal doctor?" asked the Cat's-meat-Man.

The parrot, Polynesia, was sitting in the window looking out at the rain and singing a sailor song to herself. She stopped singing and started to listen.

"You see, Doctor," the Cat's-meat-Man went on, "you know all about animals—much more than what these here vets do. That book you wrote—about cats—why, it's wonderful! I can't read or write myself—or maybe *I'd* write some books. But my wife, Theodosia, she's a scholar, she is. And she read your book to me. Well, it's wonderful—that's all can be said—wonderful. You might have been a cat yourself. You know the way they think. And listen: you can make a lot of money doctoring animals. Do you know that? You see, I'd send all the old women who had sick cats or dogs to you. And if they didn't get sick fast enough, I could put something in the meat I sell 'em to make 'em sick, see?"

"Oh, no," said the Doctor quickly. "You mustn't do that. That wouldn't be right."

"Oh, I didn't mean real sick," answered the Cat's-meat-Man. "Just a little something to make them droopy-like was what I had reference to. But as you say, maybe it ain't quite fair on the animals. But they'll get sick anyway, because the old women always give 'em too much to eat. And look, all the farmers round about who had lame horses and weak lambs—they'd come. Be an animal doctor."

When the Cat's-meat-Man had gone, the parrot flew off the window onto the Doctor's table and said, "That man's got sense. That's what you ought to do. Be an animal doctor. Give the silly people up—if they haven't brains enough to see you're the best doctor in the world. Take care of animals instead—*they'll* soon find it out. Be an animal doctor."

"Oh, there are plenty of animal doctors," said John Dolittle, putting the flower pots outside on the window sill to get the rain.

"Yes, there *are* plenty," said Polynesia, "but none of them are any good at all. Now listen, Doctor, and I'll tell you something. Did you know that animals can talk?"

"I knew that parrots can talk," said the Doctor.

"Oh, parrots can talk in two languages—people's language and bird language," said Polynesia proudly. "If I say, 'Polly wants a cracker,' you understand me. But hear this: *Ka-Ka oi-ee, fee-fee?*"

"Good gracious!" cried the Doctor. "What does that mean?"

"That means, 'Is the porridge hot yet?'—in bird language."

"My! You don't say so!" said the Doctor. "You never talked that way to me before."

"What would have been the good?" said Polynesia,

dusting some cracker crumbs off her left wing. "You wouldn't have understood me if I had."

"Tell me some more," said the Doctor, all excited; and he rushed over to the dresser drawer and came back with the butcher's book and a pencil. "Now don't go too fast—and I'll write it down. This is interesting—very interesting—something quite new. Give me the birds' A B C first—slowly now."

So that was the way the Doctor came to know that animals had a language of their own and could talk to one another. And all that afternoon, while it was raining, Polynesia sat on the kitchen table giving him bird words to put down in the book. At teatime, when the dog, Jip, came in, the parrot said to the Doctor, "See; *he's* talking to you."

"Looks to me as though he were scratching his ear," said the Doctor.

"But animals don't always speak with their mouths," said the parrot in a high voice, raising her eyebrows. "They talk with their ears, with their feet, with their tails—with everything. Sometimes they don't *want* to make a noise. Do you see now the way he's twitching up one side of his nose?"

"What's that mean?" asked the Doctor.

"That means, 'Can't you see that it has stopped raining?'" Polynesia answered. "He is asking you a question. Dogs nearly always use their noses for asking questions."

After a while, with the parrot's help, the Doctor got to learn the language of the animals so well that he could talk to them himself and understand everything they said. Then he gave up being a people's doctor altogether. As soon as the Cat's-meat-Man had told everyone that John Dolittle was going to become an animal doctor, old ladies began to bring him their pet pugs and poodles who had eaten too much cake; and farmers came many miles to show him sick cows and sheep. One day a plow horse was brought to him; and the poor thing was terribly glad to find a man who could talk in horse language.

"You know, Doctor," said the horse, "that vet over the hill knows nothing at all. He has been treating me six weeks now—for spavins. What I need is spectacles. I am going blind in one eye. There's no reason why horses shouldn't wear glasses, the same as people. But that stupid man over the hill never even looked at my eyes. He kept on giving me pills. I tried to tell him, but he couldn't understand a word of horse language. What I need is spectacles."

"Of course, of course," said the Doctor. "I'll get you some at once."

"I would like a pair like yours," said the horse, "only green. They'll keep the sun out of my eyes while I'm plowing the fifty-acre field."

"Certainly," said the Doctor. "Green ones you shall have."

"You know, the trouble is, sir," said the horse as the Doctor opened the front door to let him out, "the trouble is that *anybody* thinks he can doctor animals—just because the animals don't complain. As a matter of fact it takes a much cleverer man to be a really good animal doctor than it does to be a good people's doctor. My farmer's boy thinks he knows all about horses. I wish you could see him— his face is so fat he looks as though he had no eyes— and he has got as much brain as a potato bug. He tried to put a mustard plaster on me last week."

"Where did he put it?" asked the Doctor.

"Oh, he didn't put it anywhere—on me," said the horse. "He only tried to. I kicked him into the duck pond."

"Well, well!" said the Doctor.

"I'm a pretty quiet creature as a rule," said the horse—"very patient with people—don't make much fuss. But it was bad enough to have that vet giving me the wrong medicine. And when that red-faced booby started to monkey with me, I just couldn't bear it any more."

"Did you hurt the boy much?" asked the Doctor.

"Oh, no," said the horse. "I kicked him in the right place. The vet's looking after him now. When will my glasses be ready?"

"I'll have them for you next week," said the Doctor. "Come in again Tuesday. Good morning!"

Then John Dolittle got a fine big pair of green spectacles, and the plow horse stopped going blind in one eye and could see as well as ever. And soon it became a common sight to see farm animals wearing glasses in the country round Puddleby; and a blind horse was a thing unknown.

And so it was with all the other animals that were brought to him.

As soon as they found that he could talk their language, they told him where the pain was and how they felt, and of course it was easy for him to cure them.

Now all these animals went back and told their brothers and friends that there was a doctor in the little house with the big garden who really *was* a doctor. And whenever any creatures got sick—not only horses and cows and dogs, but all the little

things of the fields, like harvest mice and water moles, badgers, and bats—they came at once to his house on the edge of the town, so that his big garden was nearly always crowded with animals trying to get in to see him. There were so many that came that he had to have special doors made for the different kinds.

He wrote "HORSES" over the front door, "COWS" over the side door, and "SHEEP" on the kitchen door. Each kind of animal had a separate door— even the mice had a tiny tunnel made for them into the cellar, where they waited patiently in rows for the Doctor to come round to them.

So, in a few years' time, every living thing for miles and miles got to know about John Dolittle, M.D. And the birds who flew to other countries in the winter told animals in foreign lands of the wonderful doctor of Puddleby-on-the-Marsh who could understand their talk and help them in their troubles.

In this way he became famous among the animals—all over the world—better known even than he had been among the folks of the West Country. And he was happy and liked his life very much.

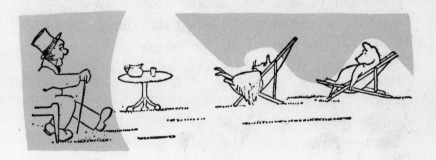

Going Too Far

A woman who lived in Holland, of old,
Polished her brass till it shone like gold.
She washed her pig after all his meals
In spite of his energetic squeals.
She scrubbed her doorstep into the ground,
And the children's faces, pink and round,
She washed so hard that in several cases
She polished their features off their faces—
Which gave them an odd appearance, though
She thought they were really neater so!
Then her passion for cleaning quickly grew,
And she scrubbed and polished the village through,
Until, to the rage of all the people,
She cleaned the weather vane off the steeple.

As she looked at the sky one summer's night
She thought that the stars shone out less bright;
And she said with a sigh, "If I were there,
I'd rub them up till the world should stare."
That night a storm began to brew,
And a wind from the ocean blew and blew
Till, when she came to her door next day
It whisked her up, and blew her away—
Up and up in the air so high
That she vanished, at last, in the stormy sky.
Since then it's said that each twinkling star
And the big white moon, shine brighter far.
But the neighbors shake their heads in fear
She may rub so hard they will disappear!

Ben and Me

I Begin My Career

Since the recent death of my lamented friend and patron, Ben Franklin, many so-called historians have attempted to write accounts of his life and his achievements. Most of these are wrong in so many respects that I feel the time has now come for me to take pen in paw and set things right.

All of these ill-informed scribblers seem astonished at Ben's great fund of information, at his brilliant decisions, at his seeming knowledge of all that went on about him. Had they asked me, I could have told them. It was ME.

For many years I was his closest friend and adviser and, if I do say it, I was in great part responsible for his success and fame.

Not that I wish to claim too much. I simply hope to see justice done, credit given where credit is due, and that's to me—mostly.

Ben was undoubtedly a splendid fellow, a great man, a patriot and all that; but he *was* undeniably stupid at times, and had it not been for me—well, here's the true story, and you can judge for yourself.

I was the oldest of twenty-six children. My parents, in naming us, went right through the alphabet. I, being first, was Amos, and the others went along through Bathsheba, Claude, Daniel—and so forth down to the babies: Xenophon, Ysobel, and Zenas.

We lived in the vestry of Old Christ Church on Second Street, in Philadelphia—behind the paneling. With that number of mouths to feed we were naturally not a very prosperous family. In fact we were quite poor—as poor as church mice.

But it was not until the Hard Winter of 1745 that things really became desperate. That was a winter long to be remembered for its severity, and night after night my poor father would come in tired and wet with his little sack practically empty.

We were driven to eating prayer books, and when those gave out, we took to the minister's sermons.

That was, for me, the final straw. The prayer books were tough, but those sermons!

Being the oldest, it seemed fitting that I should go out into the world and make my own way. Perhaps I could in some way help the others. At least, it left one less to be provided for.

So, saying farewell to all of them—my mother and father and all the children from Bathsheba to Zenas—I set forth on the coldest, windiest night of a cold and windy winter.

Little did I dream at that moment of all the strange people and experiences I should encounter before ever I returned to that little vestry home! All I thought of were my cold paws, my empty stomach—and those sermons.

I have never known how far I traveled that night, for, what with the cold and hunger, I must have become slightly delirious. The first thing I remember clearly was being in a kitchen and smelling CHEESE! It didn't take long to find it. It was only a bit of rind and fairly dry, but how I ate!

Refreshed by this, my first real meal in many a day, I began to explore the house. It was painfully bare; clean, but bare with very little furniture, and that all hard and shiny; no soft things or dusty corners where a chap could curl up and have a good warm nap. It was cold, too. Almost as cold as outdoors. Upstairs were two rooms. One was dark, and from it came the sound of snoring; the other had a light and the sound of sneezing. I chose the sneezy one.

In a large chair close to the fireplace sat a short, thick, round-faced man, trying to write by the light of a candle. Every few moments he would sneeze, and his square-rimmed glasses would fly off. Reaching for these, he would drop his pen; by the time he found that and got settled to write, the candle would flicker from the draft; and when that calmed down, the sneezing would start again. And so it went. He was not accomplishing much in the way of writing.

Of course I recognized him.

Everyone in Philadelphia knew the great Doctor Benjamin Franklin, author, soldier, statesman, inventor, scientist, editor, printer, and philosopher.

He didn't look great or famous that night, though. He just looked cold—and a bit silly.

He was wrapped in a sort of dressing gown with a dirty fur collar, and on his head was perched an odd-looking fur cap.

The cap interested me, for I was still chilled to the bone, and this room was just as bleak as the rest of the house. It was a rather disreputable-looking affair, that cap; but in one side of it I had spied a hole—just about my size. Up the back of the chair I went, and under cover of the next

fit of sneezes, in I slid. What a cozy place that
was! Plenty of room to move about a bit; just
enough air; such soft fur; and such warmth!

"Here," said I to myself, "is my home. No
more cold streets or cellars or vestries. HERE I
stay."

At the moment, of course, I didn't realize how
true this was to prove. All I realized was that I
was warm, well-fed, and—oh, so sleepy!

And so to bed.

We Invent the Franklin Stove

I slept late the next morning. When I woke up, my fur-cap home was hanging on the bedpost, and I in it. Dr. Franklin was again crouched over the fire attempting to write between fits of sneezing and glasses-hunting. The fire, what there was of it, was smoking, and the room was as cold as ever.

"Not wishing to be critical—" I said. "But perhaps a bit of wood on that smoky ember that you seem to consider a fire might——"

"WASTE NOT, WANT NOT," said he, severe.

"Well, just suppose," I said. "Just suppose you spend two or three weeks in bed with *pewmonia*— would that be a waste or——"

"It would be," said he, putting on a log, "whatever your name might be."

"Amos," said I. "And there'd be doctor bills——"

"BILLS!" said he, shuddering, and put on two more logs, quick. The fire blazed up then, and the room became a little better, but not much.

"Dr. Franklin," I said, "that fireplace is wrong."

"You might call me Ben—just plain Ben," said he. "What's wrong with it?"

"Well, for one thing, most of the heat goes up the chimney. And for another, you can't get *around* it. Outside our church there used to be a Hot-chestnut Man. Sometimes, when business was rushing, he'd drop a chestnut. Pop was always on the lookout, and almost before it touched the ground he'd have it in his sack—and down to the vestry with it. There he'd put it in the middle of the floor—and we'd all gather round for the warmth.

"Twenty-eight of us it would heat, and the room as well. It was all because it was *out in the open*, not stuck in a hole in the wall like that fireplace."

"Amos," he interrupted, excited, "there's an idea there! But we couldn't move the fire out into the middle of the room."

"We could if there were something to put it in, iron or something."

"But the smoke?" he objected.

"Pipe," said I, and curled up for another nap. I didn't get it, though.

Ben rushed off downstairs, came back with a great big armful of junk, dumped it on the floor, and was off for more. No one could have slept, not even a dormouse. After a few trips he had a big pile of things there. There were scraps of iron, tin, and wire. There were a couple of old warming pans, an iron oven, three flatirons, six potlids, a wire bird-cage, and an anvil. There were saws, hammers, pincers, files, drills, nails, screws, bolts, bricks, sand, and an old broken sword.

He drew out a sort of plan and went to work. With the clatter he made there was no chance of a nap, so I helped all I could, picking up the nuts and screws and tools that he dropped—and his glasses.

Ben was a fair terror for work, once he was interested. It was almost noon before he stopped for a bit of rest. We looked over what had been done, and it didn't look so bad—considering.

It was shaped much like a small fireplace set up on legs, with two iron doors on the front and a smoke pipe running from the back to the fireplace. He had taken the andirons out of the fireplace and boarded that up so we wouldn't lose any heat up the chimney. Ben walked around looking at it, proud as could be, but worried. "The floor," he said. "It's the floor that troubles me, Amos. With those short legs and that thin iron bottom, the heat——"

"Down on the docks," said I, "we used to hear the ship rats telling how the sailors build their cooking-fires on board ship. A layer of sand right on the deck, bricks on top of that, and——"

"Amos," he shouted, "you've got it!" and rushed for the bricks and sand. He put a layer of sand in the bottom of the affair, the bricks on top of that, and then set the andirons in. It looked pretty promising.

"Eureka!" he exclaimed, stepping back to admire it and tripping over the saw. "Straighten things up a bit, Amos, while I run and get some logs."

"*Don't* try to run," I said. "And by the way, do you come through the pantry on the way up?"

"Why?" he asked.

"In some ways, Ben," I said, "you're fairly bright, but in others you're just plain dull. The joy of creating may be meat and drink to you; but as for me, a bit of cheese——"

He was gone before I finished, but when he came back with the logs, he had a fine slab of cheese, a loaf of rye bread, and a good big tankard of ale.

We put in some kindling and logs and lit her up. She drew fine, and Ben was so proud and excited that I had to be rather sharp with him before he would settle down to food. Even then he was up every minute, to admire it from a new angle.

Before we'd finished even one sandwich the room had warmed up like a summer afternoon.

"Amos," said he, "we've done it!"

"Thanks for the WE," I said. "I'll remember it."

We Discover Electricity

It all started with some glass tubes and a book of instructions sent to Ben by a London friend. These glass tubes he would rub with a piece of silk or fur, thereby producing many strange, and, to me, unpleasant effects. When a tube was sufficiently rubbed, small bits of paper would spring from the table and cling to it, or crackling sparks leap from it to the finger of anyone foolish enough to approach. Ben derived great amusement from rubbing a tube and touching it to the tip of my tail. Thereupon a terrible shock would run through my body; every hair and whisker would stand on end, and a convulsive contraction of all my muscles would throw me several inches into the air.

This was bad enough, but my final rebellion did not come until he, in his enthusiasm, used the fur cap to rub the tube. And I was in the cap.

"Ben," said I, "this has gone far enough. From now on, kindly omit me from these experiments. To me they seem a perfectly senseless waste of time, but if they amuse you, all right, go ahead with them. Just leave me out."

"I fear you are not a person of vision, Amos," said he. "You fail to grasp the world-wide, epoch-making importance of these experiments. You do not realize the force——"

"Oh, don't I?" I replied. "My tail is still tingling."

"I shall tear the lightning from the skies," said Ben, "and harness it to do the bidding of man."

"Personally," said I, "I think the sky's an excellent place for it."

Nothing I could say, though, served to dampen Ben's enthusiasm.

I observed that he was developing an unseemly interest in lightning. Every time a house or tree was struck, Ben was the first to reach the scene, questioning all who had been present as to how the bolt had looked, smelled, or sounded, what sensations they had felt, and so on. Then he would go into a brown study that lasted for hours, occasionally murmuring, "I wonder, I wonder."

"Wonder what?" I asked finally. It was getting on my nerves.

"Why, if lightning and electricity are the same."

"To me they are," I said promptly. "They're both annoying, horrid, dangerous nuisances that should be let strictly alone."

"There you go again, Amos. No vision."

"All right," I said, "ALL RIGHT. And if they *are* the same, and if you *do* prove it, then what?"

"Why, then," he said, "why, then, I shall go down in history as he who tamed the lightning, who——"

"If you have any notion of making a house-pet of this lightning," I said, "you can go down in history as anything you please. For myself, I will go down in the cellar—and stay there."

Two days later I was waked from my nap by a terrible clatter overhead. Investigation disclosed Ben seated on the roof, busily hammering. He had fastened a whole collection of sharp-pointed iron rods to various parts of the housetop. There were two or three on each chimney and a series of them along the ridgepole. These were all connected by a tangle of wires and rods that ran down through the trap door into our room.

"You see, Amos," he explained, while connecting wires to various instruments, "the trouble with most people is that they lack the calm observation of the trained scientific mind. Time after time I have rushed to the scene of one of these lightning strokes, and all I could gather from the bystanders was that they were 'terrible skeered.' Now by collecting a small amount of this so-called lightning with the rods which you saw on the roof and conducting it through wires to these jars and instruments, we shall be able to investigate its nature and behavior with true scientific calm.

"We shall be able to settle forever the question which is puzzling all great minds, the question of whether or not lightning is electrical."

"It has never puzzled *my* mind," I said. "Left to myself I wouldn't give it a thought. Moreover," I continued, "you might as well leave out that *we*. I resigned from these experiments a long time ago. Any observing that I do will be done in the cellar. And, as the sky has clouded up rather threateningly, I think I will retire there at once."

The storm was closer than I thought, for I had barely started when there occurred a most horrifying flash of lightning followed by a thunderclap that shook the house to its foundations. The shock threw me bodily into an empty glass jar. This was fortunate, for here I was able to observe all that went on, while the glass protected me from the flashes that followed in rapid succession.

At the first flash the liquid in Ben's jars disappeared in a great burst of yellowish steam, and the instruments bounced about wildly. As flash followed flash, blue sparks ran up and down the wires, the andirons glowed as though dipped in phosphorus, and streaks of fire shot from the candlesticks on the mantelpiece. The crashing thunder was continuous, jarring every loose object in the house. There

was now no doubt in *my* mind that lightning was electricity—in its most horrid and dangerous form.

In the confusion I had forgotten Ben. Now looking about, I was astonished to find him nowhere in sight.

At this moment a large ball of blue fire emerged from the Franklin stove, rolled across the floor, and descended the stairs, crackling and giving off a strange odor of sulphur. The unusually violent crash that followed brought a faint moan from the bed.

There I discovered Ben, or rather his feet, for they were the only part of him visible. The rest was covered by the bedclothes, while two pillows completely muffled his head.

At first I was alarmed, but as each succeeding crash brought an echoing moan and a violent trembling of the feet, I realized that all that had befallen him was a severe case of fright.

Safe in my big glass jar I thoroughly enjoyed the spectacle of Ben's terror as long as the storm raged.

As the last rumblings died away, he cautiously raised the pillows and peered forth. He was a most amusing sight.

"Now, Dr. Franklin," I jeered as he sheepishly rose from the bed, "would you lend a bit of your calm, scientific study to getting me out of this jar? And by the way, what did you observe as to the true nature of lightning?"

"Do you know, Amos," he explained, "that first flash knocked off my glasses, and of course I see very poorly without them."

"So you replaced them with a couple of pillows," I said.

He never answered me—just started picking up the remains of his apparatus.

When, some time later, a scientific writer called them "Lightning Rods," naming Ben as their inventor, he refused to take the credit. This startling display of modesty surprised many people—but not me. I knew all about it.

Big Steve, the Tunnelman

Like a stone wall a mile high, the Rockies have always stood in the way of travelers from coast to coast. Many years ago some people got the notion that if the Rockies were flattened out, travel would be a lot easier.

They called in Paul Bunyan and asked him how about it. He said sure, he could flatten them out, press out all the wrinkles as smooth as glass. But before they gave him the job, they decided to make a survey first.

So they called in Finn MacCool, the civil engineer. After surveying the entire Rockies, he came up with the answer that if the mountains were flattened out, the Rocky Mountain states would stretch

From *Big Steve: The Double Quick Tunnelman* by Marie Halun Bloch, copyright, 1952. Adapted and reprinted by permission of Coward-McCann, Inc.

eastward to the Hudson River and westward to the Sierra Nevadas. This would leave only a narrow strip on each coast for all the other states of the Union to squeeze into.

When the Texans got wind of this, they put up a big holler. They were the biggest state, and over their dead bodies would they let any other state be bigger. And then naturally all the states that would be squeezed along the coasts were dead set against the plan.

Febold Feboldson, the weather-control expert in Nebraska, loudly pointed out that the Rockies are a storm-stopper. Take them away and the storms from the far northwest would whistle across the smoothed-out Rockies with nothing to stop them. Nebraska would be buffeted by tornadoes and who knows what from two sides instead of just one.

Well, the idea had to be dropped, and travelers still had to climb first up, then down the Rockies to get to where they were going.

One day Big Steve, the double-quick tunnelman, got his first sight of the Rockies. He and Daisy, his rock hog, approached them from the western slope. Daisy was a rare animal that looked almost like a dog. But besides dog, she was part mole, part ground hog, and part gopher—the mole part being the most important. Daisy was a natural-born tunneler.

When the tunnelman saw the towering mountains of granite, his first thought, naturally, was to make a double-quick beeline tunnel through them.

"Here's our chance, Daisy," he said. "I'll start you tunneling from the eastern slope, and I'll tunnel in from this side. When we meet in the middle, we'll have a real double-quick beeline tunnel."

The rock hog's excited barking echoed against the foothills. She was all for it.

"O.K., then," Big Steve said. "We'll cross over and I'll get you started on your end."

At the top of the second range they came upon a white-haired, long-haired hermit. He was rocking in a rocking chair on the brink of the canyon and singing at the top of his lungs. When he saw Big Steve with his rock hog, he stopped.

"People again!" he exclaimed.
"Getting so crowded around here
a body can't even turn around. And
what's that beast you got with you?"

"My rock hog—the best tunneler you'll ever meet,
mister! Come along, Daisy."

"What's your hurry?" drawled the hermit. "Spend
the night in my cabin. You won't get much farther
today anyway. It's getting on to nighttime."

Big Steve was surprised at the hermit's sudden
friendliness. But the old man was right—the sun
had already sunk behind the back range. "O.K.,"
Big Steve said. "Much obliged."

That night the hermit said, "I know a place that
would make your eyes bug out. Full o' gold it is.
I've been prospecting the Rockies for a hundred

years, and this is the richest find yet." His eyes glittered. "All I got to do is dig it out and I'll be the richest man in the world!"

"Why don't you, then?" asked Big Steve.

"It's smack in the middle of this mountain, that's why!" replied the hermit. "But it's there all right. My electric divining rod nearly jerked out of my hand when I walked over the spot."

Big Steve was taking all this with a grain of salt. Daisy lay alert at his feet, her eyes shining. The hermit kept eying the tunnelman and his rock hog, as if some sort of plan were forming in his mind.

Finally he said, "Tunnelman, did you say?"

"That's right!"

"And this here rock hog of yours——?"

"The best tunneler you ever saw!" boasted Big Steve. "For hard stuff like this Pike's Peak granite you got around here—she's tops."

"Tell you what, stranger," said the hermit, "how about you and me going divvies?"

"Divvies? You mean——?"

"I mean, you dig me a tunnel to this treasure room of mine and you can have half the gold out of it. How's that for a bargain?"

Daisy began whacking her tail against the floor.

It was plain to Big Steve that the old man had the gold fever and had it bad. And to people like that, everything that glistens is gold. Big Steve knew that once he started tunneling for gold, he'd spend the rest of his life at it. He had other plans.

"Well?" asked the hermit.

Big Steve shook his head. "I'd sure like to oblige you," he said, "but I can't."

Daisy laid her chin on her paws and sighed.

That night she slept so restlessly that Big Steve finally got up to look at her. Her nose was dry, and she was breathing hoarsely. He put a hand on her brow. It was so hot it scorched his hand. Then he knew the dreadful thing that had happened to his rock hog. She had caught the gold fever!

He glanced over at the hermit's bunk. The old man was muttering between snores, "Gold! Gold!"

Big Steve knew that the only cure for Daisy was to get her away from the hermit who had infected her with this dread disease. At the first sign of dawn, he would leave the Rockies.

But in the meantime he tried one thing. He gave Daisy a straight-off-the-shoulder talk.

"Listen, Daisy, old girl," he whispered, "gold is evil. Gold is a disease. Gold is bright and yellow, but it's hard and cold."

It was no use. Every time he said the word "gold," Daisy panted eagerly and thumped her tail on the floor. He gave up and settled back into a fitful sleep. When he woke up again, a faint light had already crept into the cabin.

"Daisy?" No answer.

He jumped out of bed. The hermit's bunk was empty, and Daisy was nowhere in sight. "He stole her!" yelled Big Steve, hurrying into his clothes.

It was clear that the old man had stolen Daisy to get her to drive a tunnel to his treasure. What was it the hermit had said about his treasure cave? "Smack in the middle of this mountain."

Big Steve scrambled down into the canyon and soon discovered a hole in the canyon wall. Around the sides of the hole, sure enough, were the marks of Daisy's sharp claws. Hurrying into the passage, he saw that the tunnel zigzagged sharply. "Daisy's forgot the beeline!" he thought.

With all that zigzagging, Big Steve decided that the quickest way to head her and the old man off would be a beeline tunnel. Rushing back out into the canyon, he unfolded his rock reamer and drove it feverishly, again and again, into the granite to the right of Daisy's tunnel. Suddenly it seemed to go into empty space. He thought that he had cut into Daisy's tunnel. But when he stepped forward, he found himself in the open, on the eastern slope of the Rockies. "Pshaw!" he said. "Missed 'em!"

He chose a new spot and began to tunnel a beeline back into the mountain. Once more the reamer seemed to hit empty space. "If I keep this up," he thought, "this mountain'll be nothing but a sieve."

Stepping through the opening, he found himself in a cavern. When he flashed his light over the walls and the chunks of rock piled about, they sparkled back at him.

"Nothing but fool's gold!" Big Steve exclaimed after examining a rock. "Poor old man."

From somewhere in the mountain came the sound of tunneling. The next moment, amid a shower of rocks, Daisy burst into the cave. Right behind her was the old man, carrying a torch. The tunnelman knew that the gold fever had got complete hold of his rock hog. She did not even see him. The old man began tossing up chunks of fool's gold, shouting, "Gold! Gold! We're rich!"

Daisy frisked around madly, never heeding the chunks of rock that clattered down on her tunnelman's hat.

Big Steve was disgusted at the sight. Grabbing up Daisy, he ran back into the tunnel he had just made from the eastern slope. He did not slacken his pace till the old man's shouts of joy had faded completely away. Suddenly a glitter in the tunnel wall caught Big Steve's eye, and a queer feeling began to come over him. His throat was dry, and he felt light-headed.

"Wonder if it *is* gold," he said aloud.

Before he knew what he was doing, he'd begun to bore a side passage off the tunnel.

"We'll follow this streak and see if it gets any bigger," he said. Daisy yelped joyfully. Then Big Steve noticed an even brighter spot in the wall of the new tunnel. He forgot his beeline and began to zigzag through the mountain, following first one and then another sparkling vein of rock. Several times they tunneled right through the mountain to the outside. But each time they tunneled right back in.

In the tunnel they were working on, water began to trickle through the cracks in the rock. But Big Steve did not notice it. This shows how far gone he was. No tunnelman would overlook a thing like that. It meant that a little water was working its way down, or that an underground river, on a higher level, was seeking a way into the new tunnel.

Suddenly there was the thunder of breaking rock and then the gurgle of water growing to a roar.

A river had found its
way through. The water
came tumbling into the passage
and rushed straight for the tunnelman and his rock hog. It swept them
along its swift way through the tunnel. Big
Steve grabbed hold of Daisy and hung onto her
as they were rushed helplessly along.

At last there was a glimpse of daylight ahead. In
another moment the river had carried them through
the tunnel entrance in the eastern slope, then out
of the mountain, through the foothills, and into the
state of Nebraska.

In the middle of Nebraska it finally ran out of
water, and they ground to a stop. Big Steve felt
refreshed. He looked at Daisy. Her nose was
moist, and the fever glitter had left her eyes.

Now that they were both safe again, Big Steve got mad at Daisy for what she had done. "I've a good mind to ship you home and go on alone."

Daisy hung her head. She was sorry that she had spoiled Big Steve's plans for a beeline tunnel. But the tunnelman could never stay mad very long. "Well," he said, rubbing Daisy between the ears, "maybe it wasn't your fault at that. Come along."

And they started walking eastward across the state of Nebraska.

Later, the first of the beeline tunnels Big Steve had bored from the middle of the Rockies to the eastern slope was lengthened so that it would go through to the western slope also. Ever since, instead of puffing up, then braking slowly down, trains go into the tunnel and right through the Rockies. This saves lots of time, and everybody's happy.

All except the hermit. He doesn't fancy all those people traveling through his mountain. Sometimes, just to get away from them, he goes down into the zigzag tunnels, and on clear days you can hear him whooping and hollering down there.

BOOKS TO READ

Here are some good books that provide more of the same fun and adventure we find in the new *People and Progress*.

Young Americans Today

A Nickel for Alice.   Frances Salomon Murphy.
A Place for Peter.   Elizabeth Yates.
A Race for Bill.   May Nickerson Wallace.
Bigity Anne.   Helen F. Daringer.
Deer Mountain Hideaway.   Elizabeth Hubbard Lansing.
Five Boys in a Cave.   Richard Church.
One Hundred White Horses.   Mildred Lawrence.
Ready-Made Family.   Frances Salomon Murphy.
Rowena Carey.   Ruth Holberg.
Sparkplug of the Hornets.   Stephen W. Meader.
Stepsister Sally.   Helen F. Daringer.
The Saturdays.   Elizabeth Enright.
The Wooden Locket.   Alice Alison Lide and Margaret Alison Johansen.
Told under Spacious Skies.   Association for Childhood Education.

Early Adventures in Progress

America Travels.   Alice Dalgliesh.
Captain Ramsay's Daughter.   Elizabeth Torjesen.
Crissy at the Wheel.   Mildred Lawrence.
Lucky Year.   Dorothy Aldis.
Mr. Bell Invents the Telephone.   Katherine B. Shippen.
Steamboat South.   Madye Lee Chastain.
Sybil Ludington's Ride.   Erick Berry.
The Panama Canal.   Bob Considine.
The Real Book about Inventions.   Samuel Epstein and Beryl Williams.
The Real Book about Trains.   Davis Cole.
The Story Behind Great Inventions.   Elizabeth Montgomery.

The Train That Never Came Back and Other Railroad Stories.
   Freeman H. Hubbard.
Thomas Alva Edison, Inventor. Ruth Cromer Weir.

Man-made Wonders of Today

Bulldozer. Stephen W. Meader.
Diesel-Electric 4030. Henry Billings.
Flight Today and Tomorrow. Margaret O. Hyde.
Machines at Work. Mary Elting.
Mining the Iron Mask. George Cory Franklin.
Oliver Sounds Off! Jack Bechdolt.
Perhaps I'll Be a Railroad Man. Ray Bethers.
Rod, the Sky Lad. Helen Hall and W. F. Hall.
The First Book of Airplanes. Jeanne Bendick.
The Light at Tern Rock. Julia L. Sauer.
Trains at Work. Mary Elting.
Your Telephone and How It Works. Herman and Nina
   Schneider.

Fun and Fancy

Ben and Me. Robert Lawson.
Big Steve: The Double Quick Tunnelman. Marie Bloch.
Charlotte's Web. E. B. White.
Homer the Tortoise. Margaret J. Baker.
Mr. Revere and I. Robert Lawson.
Sam Patch, the High, Wide, and Handsome Jumper. Arna
   Bontemps and Jack Conroy.
The Borrowers. Mary Norton.
The Fast Sooner Hound. Arna Bontemps and Jack Conroy.
The Little Prince. Antoine de Saint-Exupéry.
The Space Ship under the Apple Tree. Louis Slobodkin.
The Tough Winter. Robert Lawson.
The Twenty-one Balloons. William Pène du Bois.
The Voyages of Dr. Dolittle. Hugh Lofting.
Which Was Witch? Tales of Ghosts and Magic from Korea.
   Eleanore M. Jewett.

GLOSSARY

Full Pronunciation Key

The pronunciation of each word is shown just after the word, in this way: **ab bre vi ate** (ə brē′vi āt). The letters and signs used are pronounced as in the words below. The mark ′ is placed after a syllable with primary or heavy accent, as in the example above. The mark ′ after a syllable shows a secondary or lighter accent, as in **ab bre vi a tion** (ə brē′vi ā′shən).

a	hat, cap	j	jam, enjoy	u	cup, butter
ā	age, face	k	kind, seek	ủ	full, put
ã	care, air	l	land, coal	ü	rule, move
ä	father, far	m	me, am	ū	use, music
		n	no, in		
b	bad, rob	ng	long, bring		
ch	child, much			v	very, save
d	did, red	o	hot, rock	w	will, woman
		ō	open, go	y	young, yet
		ô	order, all	z	zero, breeze
e	let, best	oi	oil, voice	zh	measure, seizure
ē	equal, be	ou	house, out		
ėr	term, learn				
		p	paper, cup	ə	represents:
f	fat, if	r	run, try		a in about
g	go, bag	s	say, yes		e in taken
h	he, how	sh	she, rush		i in pencil
		t	tell, it		o in lemon
i	it, pin	th	thin, both		u in circus
ī	ice, five	ᴛʜ	then, smooth		

This pronunciation key is from the *Thorndike-Barnhart Junior Dictionary*. Special acknowledgment is made to Clarence L. Barnhart, editor of the Thorndike-Barnhart Dictionaries, for his assistance in the preparation of this glossary.

ac ces so ry (ak ses′ə ri), something added; a finishing touch: *All the accessories to her costume—gloves, handkerchief, and purse—were perfectly matched in color.*

ac cor di on (ə kôr′di ən), musical instrument with keys, metal reeds, and a bellows. An accordion is played by forcing air through the reeds by means of the bellows.

a chieve (ə chēv′), **1.** do; get done; carry out: *John soon learned that you cannot achieve much without work.* **2.** reach (a certain end) by one's own efforts; gain by effort: *He achieved fame as an artist at an early age.*

ac knowl edge (ak nol′ij), **1.** admit to be true: *He acknowledges his mistakes.* **2.** recognize the authority or claims of: *We acknowledged him to be the best player on the team.* **3.** express thanks for. **4.** make known that one has received (a favor, gift, message, etc.).

a ghast (ə gast′), frightened; struck with surprise or horror; filled with terror.

Ak ron (ak′rən), city in northeastern Ohio.

Al ba ny (ôl′bə ni), the capital of New York State.

Al lah (al′ə), Mohammedan name for God.

al ma nac (ôl′mə nak), calendar of days, weeks, and months, often with information about the weather, sun, moon, stars, tides, and other facts.

an ces tor (an′ses tər), person from whom one is descended. Your father, your mother, your grandfathers, your grandmothers, and so on back, are your ancestors.

and i rons (and′ī′ərnz), pair of metal supports for wood in a fireplace. See the picture.

Andirons

an vil (an′vəl), an iron block on which metals are hammered and shaped. See the picture.

ANVIL

ap pa ra tus (ap′ə rā′təs or ap′-ə rat′əs), things necessary to carry out a purpose. Tools, special instruments, and machines are apparatus. A chemical set and a grocer's scales are apparatus.

arch bish op (ärch′bish′əp), clergyman of the highest rank, at the head of a church district.

as tral (as′trəl), of the stars; starry.

au di tion (ô dish′ən), **1.** hearing. **2.** hearing to test the ability of a musician, speaker, etc.

au thor i ty (ə thôr′ə ti), **1.** power; control: *A father has authority over his children.* **2.** right: *A policeman has the authority to arrest fast drivers.* **3.** person who has power or right. **4.** source of correct information or wise advice: *A good dictionary is an authority on the meanings of words.*

au to mat ic (ô′tə mat′ik), **1.** acting or moving of itself: *an automatic lock, an automatic pump.* **2.** done without thought or attention: *Breathing and swallowing are usually automatio.*

au to mat i cal ly (ô′tə mat′ik li), in an automatic manner.

badg er (baj′ər), **1.** hairy, gray animal that digs holes in the ground to live in. **2.** its fur. **3.** keep on questioning; keep on teasing or annoying: *An agent has been badgering me for the last three weeks to buy a new car.*

barge (bärj), **1.** large, flat-bottomed boat for carrying freight on rivers and canals. **2.** push oneself rudely: *Don't barge in where you're not wanted.*

bar ri er (bar′i ər), **1.** something that stands in the way; something stopping progress or preventing approach: *Lack of water was a barrier to the settlement of that region.* **2.** something that separates or keeps apart: *The Atlantic Ocean is a barrier between Europe and America.*

bi plane (bī′plān′), airplane that has two wings, one above the other.

bleak (blēk), **1.** bare; swept by winds: *The rocky peaks of high mountains are bleak.* **2.** chilly; cold: *a bleak wind.* **3.** dreary; dismal.

booth (büth), **1.** place where goods are sold or exhibited at a fair, market, etc. **2.** small, closed place for a telephone, etc. **3.** small, closed place for voting at elections.

bot a ny (bot′ə ni), the science of plants; the study of plants and of plant life.

buf fet (buf′it), **1.** a blow of the hand. **2.** strike with the hand. **3.** a knock, stroke, or hurt. **4.** knock about, strike, or hurt: *The waves buffeted him.*

bul le tin (bùl′ə tən), short statement of news.

bu reau (būr′ō), **1.** chest of drawers for clothes. It often has a mirror. **2.** an office: *Ask about train fares at the Travel Bureau.* **3.** government department: *The Weather Bureau makes reports on weather conditions.*

ca ble (kā′bəl), **1.** strong, thick rope, often made of wires twisted together. **2.** message sent across the sea by cable. **3.** send such a message.

ca boose (kə büs′), small car on a freight train in which the trainmen can rest and sleep.

ca liph or **ca lif** (kā′lif), the ruler of a Mohammedan state.

ca nal (kə nal′), waterway dug across land for ships or small boats to go through, or to carry water to places that need it.

cap size (kap sīz′), upset; overturn; turn bottom side up.

cap tive (kap′tiv), **1.** prisoner: *The army brought back a thousand captives.* **2.** held as prisoner; made a prisoner: *captive soldiers.*

ca reer (kə rēr′), **1.** general course of action through life: *It is interesting to read of the careers of great men and women.* **2.** occupation; profession: *Dick chose the navy for his career.*

cat walk (kat′wôk′), narrow place to walk on a bridge or machine or in an airship.

cen ten ni al (sen ten′i əl), **1.** having to do with 100 years or the 100th anniversary. **2.** 100 years old. **3.** 100th anniversary: *The town is celebrating its centennial.*

char ac ter (kar′ik tər), **1.** The special ways in which a person feels, thinks, and acts, considered as good or bad, make up his character: *The judge was a man of fine character.* **2.** person in a play or book. **3.** person with special or notable qualities.

chem i cal (kem′ə kəl), **1.** substance obtained by changing or combining other substances. Sulphuric acid, sodium bicarbonate, borax, etc., are chemicals. **2.** having to do with or containing chemicals.

che wink (chi wingk′), bird of North America with a cry that sounds somewhat like its name. See the picture.

Chewink (8 in. long)

chime (chīm), **1.** set of bells tuned to the musical scale and played usually by hammers or simple machinery. **2.** the music made by a set of tuned bells. **3.** ring out musically: *The bells chimed midnight.* **4.** be in harmony or agreement: *His ideas chimed in beautifully with mine.*

cir cu late (sėr′kū lāt),   **1.** go around. Water circulates in the pipes of a building. **2.** send around from person to person or place to place: *He circulated the news of the holiday.*

cit rus (sit′rəs),   **1.** any tree that bears lemons, limes, oranges, or similar fruit. **2. citrus fruit,** the fruit of such a tree.

clar i net (klar′ə-net′), wooden wind instrument played by means of holes and keys. See the picture.

Man playing
a clarinet

cock pit (kok′pit′), small, open place in an airplane, boat, etc., where the pilot or passengers sit.

col lapse (kə laps′),   **1.** fall in; shrink together suddenly: *The chair collapsed when my uncle sat down on it.* **2.** falling in: *Six people were killed by the collapse of the building.* **3.** break down; fail suddenly: *Both his health and his business collapsed within a year.* **4.** breakdown; failure.

col lide (kə līd′), rush against; hit or strike violently together: *In running around the corner, John collided with another boy.*

col o ny (kol′ə ni),   **1.** group of people who leave their own country and go to settle in another land, but who still remain citizens of their own country. **2.** the settlement made by such people. **3.** one of the thirteen original settlements on the Atlantic Coast that later became the United States.

col um bine (kol′əm bīn),   plant whose flowers have petals with tube-like ends. Wild columbines have red-and-yellow or blue-and-white flowers.

col umn (kol′əm),   **1.** slender, upright structure; pillar. Columns are usually made of stone, wood, or metal, and used as supports or ornaments to a building. **2.** anything that seems slender and upright like a column: *a column of smoke.* **3.** soldiers or ships following one another in a single line. **4.** slender part of a page reading from top to bottom.

com bus ti ble (kəm bus′tə bəl),   **1.** capable of taking fire and burning: *Gasoline is highly combustible.* **2.** a combustible substance.

com pete (kəm pēt′),   **1.** try to win: *John was competing against Tim for the prize in arithmetic.* **2.** take part (in a contest): *Shall you compete in the race?*

com po si tion (kom′pə zish′ən),   **1.** the make-up of anything; what is in it: *The composition of this candy includes sugar, chocolate, and milk.* **2.** thing composed, such as a piece of music, writing, etc.

con grat u late (kən grach′ů lāt), express one's pleasure at the good fortune or happiness of (a person): *I congratulated Mary on her success.*

con spir a tor (kən spir′ə tər), one who conspires; plotter.

con spire (kən spīr′), plan secretly with others to do something wrong; plot.

con tract (kon′trakt for 1, 2, and 3, kən trakt′ for 4, 5, and 6), **1.** an agreement. In a contract two or more people agree to do or not to do certain things. **2.** written agreement that can be enforced by law. **3.** make a contract. **4.** form; enter into; start: *to contract a bad habit.* **5.** draw together; make shorter: *to contract the brows.* **6.** shrink; become shorter or smaller.

---

hat, āge, cāre, fär; let, ēqual, tėrm; it, īce; hot, ōpen, ôrder; oil, out; cup, pût, rüle, ūse; ch, child; ng, long; sh, she; th, thin; ᵺ, then; zh, measure; ə represents *a* in about, *e* in taken, *i* in pencil, *o* in lemon, *u* in circus.

con trac tion (kən trak'shən), **1.** process of contracting. Cold causes the contraction of liquids, gases, metals, etc.; heat causes expansion. **2.** state of being contracted: *The contraction of mercury by cold makes it go down in thermometers.* **3.** something contracted; a shortened form. *Can't is a contraction of cannot.*

con ven tion (kən ven'shən), **1.** a meeting arranged for some particular purpose: *A political party holds a convention to choose its candidates for public offices.* **2.** general consent; custom: *Convention now permits short hair for women, but it used to be thought queer.*

con vul sive (kən vul'siv), violently disturbing.

crest (krest), **1.** tuft or mane on the head of an animal; a rooster's comb. **2.** top of a hill or a wave; top part; peak; ridge; summit.

crev ice (krev'is), narrow split or crack: *Tiny ferns grew in crevices in the old stone wall.*

crit i cal (krit'ə kəl), **1.** inclined to find fault or disapprove: *a critical disposition.* **2.** important at a time of danger or difficulty: *Delay in getting a doctor may be critical.*

cue (kū), **1.** the last words of an actor's speech in a play that serve as the signal for another actor to come on the stage or to speak. **2.** a signal like this to a singer or musician.

dark horse, unexpected winner that little is known about.

daw dle (dô'dəl), waste time; idle; loiter: *Don't dawdle over your work.*

dea con (dē'kən), officer of a church who helps the minister in church duties not connected with preaching.

dec la ra tion (dek'lə rā'shən), statement; open or public statement. The **Declaration of Independence** was a statement adopted by the American colonies on July 4, 1776,

declaring that they were free and independent of Great Britain.

def i nite ly (def'ə nit li), **1.** clearly; not vaguely. **2.** certainly.

deft (deft), skillful; nimble; clever: *The fingers of a violinist are deft.*

del e gate (del'ə gāt), **1.** one who acts for others; a representative. **2.** appoint or send (a person) as a representative: *The class delegated Mary to buy the flowers.*

de lir i ous (di lir'i əs), **1.** out of one's senses; wandering in mind; raving. **2.** wildly excited.

dem on strate (dem'ən strāt), **1.** show clearly; prove. **2.** show, advertise, or make publicly known, by carrying out a process in public: *He demonstrated his washing machine to us by washing some clothes with it.*

dep u ty (dep'ū ti), person appointed to do the work or take the place of another.

de rive (di rīv'), get; obtain.

de vice (di vīs'), a mechanical invention used for a special purpose; machine; apparatus. A can opener is a device.

de vise (di vīz'), think out; plan; invent.

Die sel (dē'zəl), Diesel engine, an engine that burns oil. Heat caused by the compression of air sets the oil on fire.

dig ni fied (dig'nə fīd), having dignity; noble; stately; of great worth.

di min ish (də min'ish), make or become smaller in size, amount, or importance.

dis patch (dis pach'), **1.** send off to some place or for some purpose. **2.** sending off a letter, a messenger, etc.: *Hurry up the dispatch of this telegram.* **3.** written message, such as special news or government business.

dis patch er (dis pach'ər), person who dispatches. A train dispatcher sends out the trains.

dis pose (dis pōz'),   **1.** put in a certain order or position; arrange: *The ships were disposed in a straight line.* **2. Dispose of** means (**1**) get rid of. (**2**) give away. (**3**) sell. (**4**) eat or drink. **3.** arrange; settle.

dis rep u ta ble (dis rep'ū tə bəl), **1.** having a bad reputation. **2.** not respectable; worn out and dirty.

di van (dī'van or də van'),   long, low, soft couch or sofa.

di vin ing rod (də vīn'ing rod), forked stick supposed to be useful in locating water, oil, metal, and other things underground.

dor mouse (dôr'mous'),   small animal somewhat like a mouse and somewhat like a squirrel. It sleeps during cold weather.

ed it (ed'it),   **1.** prepare (another person's writings) for publication: *The teacher is editing famous speeches for use in schoolbooks.* **2.** have charge of (a newspaper, magazine, etc.) and decide what shall be printed in it.

ed i tor (ed'ə tər), person who edits.

e lapse (i laps'),   pass; slip away: *Hours elapsed while he slept like a log.*

em ber (em'bər),   piece of wood or coal from a fire, still burning a little. **Embers** often means ashes in which there is still some fire.

en coun ter (en koun'tər), **1.** meet unexpectedly: *What if we should encounter a bear?* **2.** unexpected meeting.

ep och (ep'ək),   period of time in which striking things happened.

ep och-mak ing (ep'ək māk'ing), beginning an epoch; causing important changes.

eu re ka (ū rē'kə),   Greek word meaning "I have found it." It is used to express triumph concerning a discovery.

ex po si tion (eks'pə zish'ən), public show or exhibition. A world's fair is an exposition.

fam ish (fam'ish), be very hungry; starve; starve to death.

fer ti lize (fėr'tə līz),   **1.** make fertile. **2.** make (a thing) start to grow. **3.** make (the soil) richer by adding a substance that fertilizes.

flur ry (flėr'i), **1.** sudden gust of wind. **2.** light fall of rain or snow. **3.** sudden commotion. **4.** confuse; excite: *Noise in the audience flurried the actor so that he forgot his lines.*

fo gy (fō'gi), old-fashioned person; person who is behind the times.

fo li age (fō'li ij), the leaves of a plant.

for eign (fôr'ən), **1.** outside one's own country: *She has traveled much in foreign countries.* **2.** coming from outside one's own country: *a foreign ship, foreign money.* **3.** having to do with other countries: *foreign trade.*

forth with (fôrth'with'), at once.

fort night (fôrt'nīt), two weeks.

fu se lage (fū'zə läzh or fū'zə lij), body of an airplane. The wings and tail are fastened to it. The fuselage holds the passengers, cargo, etc.

ga zette (gə zet'), newspaper.

gear (gēr), **1.** an arrangement of parts for some purpose, such as harness, clothing, tools, machinery,

Gears

or household goods. **2.** wheel having teeth that fit into teeth in another wheel; wheels turning one another by teeth. **3. In gear** means connected with the motor. **Out of gear** means not connected with the motor.

---

hat, āge, cāre, fär; let, ēqual, tėrm; it, īce; hot, ōpen, ôrder; oil, out; cup, pút, rüle, ūse; ch, child; ng, long; sh, she; th, thin; ᵮH, then; zh, measure; ə represents *a* in about, *e* in taken, *i* in pencil, *o* in lemon, *u* in circus.

gen ius (jēn′yəs),   **1.** very great natural power of mind. **2.** person having such power. **3.** great natural ability: *A great actor has a genius for acting.*

ges ture (jes′chər),   **1.** motion of the body used instead of words or with words to help express an idea or a feeling. **2.** make or use gestures.

gin ger ly (jin′jər li), with extreme care or caution.

gloat (glōt),   gaze or think about intently and with satisfaction: *The miser gloated over his gold.*

go pher (gō′fər),   **1.** ratlike animal of North America with large cheek pouches. Gophers dig holes in the ground. **2.** ground squirrel.

grade crossing,   place where a railroad crosses a street or another railroad on the same level.

gran ite (gran′it),   very hard rock, used for buildings, monuments, etc. Granite is usually gray.

grav i ty (grav′ə ti),   natural force that causes objects to move or tend to move toward the center of the earth. Gravity causes objects to have weight.

guar an tee (gar′ən tē′), **1.** a backing; a promise to pay or do something if another fails to do it. **2.** stand back of; give a guarantee for: *This company guarantees its clocks for a year.* **3.** pledge to do (something); promise (that) something has been or will be: *I will guarantee to prove every statement I made.*

gui tar (gə tär′),   musical instrument with six strings, played with the fingers.

gur gle (gėr′gəl),   **1.** flow or run with a bubbling sound. **2.** bubbling sound.

ham per[1] (ham′pər),   hold back; hinder.

ham per[2] (ham′pər),   large basket with a cover.

hedge hog (hej′hog′),   **1.** small animal of the Old World with spines on its back. If attacked, hedge-hogs roll up into a bristling ball. **2.** the porcupine of North America.

European hedgehog (about 10 in. long)

heir (ār),   person who has the right to somebody's property after that one dies.

her mit (hėr′mit),   person who goes away from other people and lives by himself.

her o ine (her′ō in),   **1.** very brave girl or woman. **2.** most important girl or woman in a story or play.

hor i zon tal (hôr′ə zon′təl),   **1.** parallel to the horizon; at right angles to a vertical line. **2.** flat; level. **3.** of or at the horizon. **4.** horizontal line, plane, direction, position, etc.

←VERTICAL

HORIZONTAL

huck le ber ry (huk′əl ber′i),   **1.** a small berry like the blueberry, darker in color. **2.** the shrub it grows on.

hy drant (hī′drənt),   large pipe with a valve for drawing water; hose connection.

i den ti fy (ī den′tə fī),   recognize as being a particular person or thing; prove to be the same: *Ted identified the bag as his by telling what it contained.*

il lu mi nate (i lü′mə nāt),   **1.** light up; make bright: *The room was illuminated by four large lamps.* **2.** throw a strong light on: *The big searchlight illuminates a spot a mile away.*

il lus tra tion (il′əs trā′shən),   **1.** picture, map, etc., used to explain or decorate something. **2.** story, example, etc., used to make clear or explain something.

im pact (im′pakt), striking of one thing against another: *The impact of the two swords broke both of them.*

im plore (im plôr′), **1.** beg earnestly for: *The prisoner implored pardon.* **2.** beg (a person) to do something: *The man implored the judge to spare his life.*

in al ien a ble (in āl′yən ə bəl), that cannot be given away or taken away: *Life, liberty, and the pursuit of happiness have been called the inalienable rights of man.*

in de pend ent (in′di pen′dənt), **1.** needing, wishing, or getting no help from others: *independent work, independent thinking.* **2.** guiding, ruling, or governing one's self; not under another's rule: *The American colonies became independent of England.*

in ge nu i ty (in′jə nü′ə ti or in′jə-nü′ə ti), cleverness; skill in planning, inventing, etc.: *The boy showed much ingenuity in making toys.*

in let (in′let), narrow strip of water running from a larger body of water into the land or between islands: *The fishing village was on a small inlet of the sea.*

in nu mer a ble (i nü′mər ə bəl or i nü′mər ə bəl), too many to count; very, very many.

in tense (in tens′), **1.** very much; very great; very strong: *intense joy, intense pain, intense light.* **2.** An intense person is one who feels things very deeply and is likely to be extreme in action.

ir ri gate (ir′ə gāt), supply (land) with water by means of ditches.

ir ri ga tion (ir′ə gā′shən), supplying land with water from ditches; irrigating.

It a ly (it′ə li), country in southern Europe.

jeep (jēp), small but powerful automobile used by the army.

Jo li et (jō′li et or jō′li et′), city in northeastern Illinois.

kin dling (kin′dling), small pieces of wood for starting a fire.

lieu ten ant (lü ten′ənt), **1.** in the army, an officer next below a captain. **2.** in the navy and coast guard, an officer ranking much below a captain.

lim it (lim′it), **1.** the farthest edge or boundary; where something ends or must end: *Keep within the limits of the school grounds.* **2.** set a limit to: *We must limit the expense to $10.*

liv er y (liv′ər i), **1.** any special uniform provided for servants or members of other groups or professions. **2.** the feeding, stabling, and care of horses for pay; the hiring out of horses and carriages. **3.** stable where horses are cared for or hired out for pay.

Lon don (lun′dən), the capital of Great Britain, in southern England.

lu mi nous (lü′mə nəs), bright; shining by its own light; full of light: *The sun and stars are luminous bodies.*

main tain (mān tān′), **1.** keep; keep up; carry on: *Maintain your hold on the rope.* **2.** uphold; support: *maintain an opinion. He maintains his family.* **3.** declare to be true: *Lucy maintained that war did not pay.*

make shift (māk′shift′), something made to use for a time instead of the right thing.

Man hat tan (man hat′ən), island on which part of New York City is.

Mar co ni (mär kō′ni), Italian inventor (1874-1937) who perfected the wireless telegraph.

---

hat, āge, cãre, fär; let, ēqual, tėrm; it, īce; hot, ōpen, ôrder; oil, out; cup, pút, rüle, ūse; ch, child; ng, long; sh, she; th, thin; ᵺ, then; zh, measure; ə represents *a* in about, *e* in taken, *i* in pencil, *o* in lemon, *u* in circus.

maze (māz), network of paths through which it is difficult to find one's way: *A guide led us through a maze of caves.*

me chan ic (mə kan′ik), workman skilled with tools; especially, one who makes, repairs, and uses machines.

Mer i den (mer′ə dən), city in Connecticut.

mer it (mer′it), **1.** goodness; worth; value; that which deserves reward or praise: *Each child will get a mark according to the merit of his work.* **2.** deserve: *A hard-working boy or girl merits praise.*

me te or (mē′ti ər), shooting star; mass of stone or metal that comes toward the earth from outer space with enormous speed. Meteors become so hot from rushing through the air that they glow and often burn up.

Mich i gan (mish′ə gən), **1.** Middle Western State of the United States. **2.** one of the Great Lakes.

mild (mīld), **1.** gentle; kind: *a mild old gentleman.* **2.** calm; warm; not severe: *mild weather.* **3.** soft or sweet to the senses; not sharp, sour, bitter, or strong in taste: *mild cheese.*

min a ret (min′ə ret′), tall, slender tower attached to a Mohammedan church, from which a crier calls the people to prayer.

mir a cle (mir′ə kəl), **1.** wonderful happening that is above, against, or independent of the known laws of nature: *It would be a miracle if the sun should stand still in the heavens for an hour.* **2.** something marvelous; a wonder.

mi ser (mī′zər), person who loves money for its own sake; one who lives poorly in order to save money and keep it. A miser dislikes to spend money for anything, except to gain more money.

mo bile (mō′bəl), movable; moving easily; easy to move: *The tongue is mobile.*

mole[1] (mōl), a spot on the skin, usually brown.

mole[2] (mōl), small animal that lives underground most of the time. Moles have velvety fur and very small eyes that cannot see well.

Mole (about 7 in. long, including the tail)

more o ver (môr ō′vər), besides; also; in addition to that: *I don't want to go skating. Moreover, the ice is too thin.*

Morse (môrs), **Samuel F. B.**, American inventor (1791-1872), who made the first telegraph instrument. The Morse telegraphic alphabet or code is named after him.

muff (muf), **1.** a covering, usually of fur, into which a woman puts both hands, one at each end, to keep them warm. **2.** fail to catch (a ball) when it comes into one's hands. **3.** handle awkwardly; bungle.

na tive (nā′tiv), **1.** person born in a certain country. The natives are the people living in a place, not visitors or foreigners. **2.** belonging to one because of his country or race: *one's native language.* **3.** born in a person; natural: *native ability.*

new fan gled (nü′fang′gəld or nū′fang′gəld), lately come into fashion; of a new kind.

nib (nib), **1.** pen point. **2.** the point of anything. **3.** bird's bill.

no., number.

non-, prefix meaning: not; opposite of; lack of; as in *nonbreakable.*

no tion (nō′shən), **1.** idea; understanding: *He has no notion of what I mean.* **2.** opinion; view; belief: *One common notion is that red hair means a quick temper.* **3.** foolish idea or opinion: *That silly girl has too many notions.*

o mit (ō mit′),   **1.** leave out: *to omit a letter in a word.* **2.** fail to do; neglect: *Mary omitted making her bed.*

Ot ta wa (ot′ə wə),   city in the north central part of Illinois.

o ver tax (ō′vər taks′),   **1.** tax too heavily. **2.** put too heavy burdens on.

pa ja mas (pə jä′məz or pə jam′əz), garments to sleep in, etc., consisting of a coat and loose trousers fastened at the waist.

par al lel (par′ə lel),   **1.** at or being the same distance apart everywhere, like the two rails of a railroad track. **2.** be at the same distance from: *The street parallels the railroad.* **3.** similar:

Three sets of parallel lines

parallel cases, parallel happenings.

Par is (par′is),   the capital of France.

pas sion (pash′ən),   **1.** very strong feeling: *Hate and fear are passions.* **2.** rage; violent anger: *He flew into a passion.* **3.** very strong liking: *Ann has a passion for music.*

pa tri ot (pā′tri ət),   person who loves and loyally supports his country.

pa tron (pā′trən),   **1.** person who stands back of the work of another, perhaps helps it with money, and gives it the advantage of his approval and his name. **2.** protector.

pence (pens),   pennies.

pen du lum (pen′jù ləm),   weight so hung from a fixed point that it is free to swing to and fro. The movement of the works of a tall clock is often timed by a pendulum.

pen e trate (pen′ə trāt),   **1.** get into or through: *A bullet can penetrate a wall or two inches into a wall.* **2.** pierce through: *Our eyes could not penetrate*

the darkness. **3.** soak through; spread through: *The rain penetrated our clothes.* **4.** see into; understand: *I could not penetrate the mystery.*

per son age (pėr′sən ij),   **1.** person of importance. **2.** person. **3.** a character in a book or a play.

Phil a del phi a (fil′ə del′fi ə), the largest city in Pennsylvania and the third largest city in the United States.

phi los o pher (fə los′ə fər),   lover of wisdom; person who has a system for guiding life.

phos pho rus (fos′fə rəs), substance that burns slowly and shines in the dark.

pho tog ra pher (fə tog′rə fər), person who takes pictures with a camera.

pin cers (pin′sərz),   **1.** tool for gripping and holding tight, made like scissors

Pincers (def. 1)

but with jaws instead of blades. **2.** the large claw of lobsters and crabs that can be used to pinch or nip; pair of claws.

Pol y ne sia (pol′ə nē′zhə).

pop u lace (pop′ū lis), the common people.

post haste (pōst′hāst′),   in great haste; very speedily.

post pone (pōst pōn′),   put off till later; put off to a later time: *The baseball game was postponed because of rain.*

pot ter (pot′ər),   keep busy in a rather useless way: *She potters about the house all day, but gets very little done.*

prin ci pal (prin′sə pəl),   **1.** most important; chief; main: *Chicago is the principal city of Illinois.* **2.** chief person; one who gives orders: *the principal of a school.*

---

hat, āge, cāre, fär; let, ēqual, tėrm; it, īce; hot, ōpen, ôrder; oil, out; cup, pùt, rüle, ūse; ch, child; ng, long; sh, she; th, thin; ᴛʜ, then; zh, measure; ə represents *a* in about, *e* in taken, *i* in pencil, *o* in lemon, *u* in circus.

proc ess (pros′es), **1.** going on; moving forward: *In process of time the house will be finished.* **2.** set of actions or changes in a special order: *By what processes is cloth made from wool?* **3. In process** means (**1**) in the course or condition. (**2**) in the course or condition of being done.

prop er ty (prop′ər ti), thing or things owned; possessions.

pub lic (pub′lik), **1.** of the people: *public opinion.* **2.** belonging to the people: *public buildings.* **3.** by the people: *public help for the poor.* **4.** for the people; serving the people: *public libraries, public schools.* **5.** all the people. **6. In public** means openly; publicly; not secretly.

pul ley (pul′i), a wheel with a hollowed rim in which a rope can run, and so lift weights, or change the direction of the pull. The flag is raised to the top of a pole by a rope that goes over a small pulley. See the picture of a pulley in use.

PULLEY →

py ja mas (pə jä′məz), pajamas.

quiv er[1] (kwiv′ər), shake; shiver; tremble.

quiv er[2] (kwiv′ər), case to hold arrows.

rank[1] (rangk), **1.** a row or line, usually of soldiers, placed side by side. **2.** position; grade; class: *New York is a city of first rank.* **3.** high position: *A duke is a man of rank.* **4.** arrange in a row or line. **5.** have a certain rank: *John ranked low in spelling.*

rank[2] (rangk), **1.** large and coarse: *rank grass.* **2.** having a bad, strong taste or smell: *rank meat.*

ream er (rēm′ər), tool for shaping or enlarging a hole.

reb el (reb′əl for 1 and 2, ri bel′ for 3 and 4), **1.** person who resists or fights against authority instead of obeying: *The rebels armed themselves against the government.* **2.** defying law or authority: *the rebel army.* **3.** resist or fight against law or authority. **4.** feel a great dislike or opposition: *We rebelled at having to stay indoors on so fine a day.*

re bel lion (ri bel′yən), a fight against government; rebelling.

re ceipt (ri sēt′), **1.** written statement that money, a package, a letter, etc., has been received: *Sign the receipt for this parcel.* **2.** write on (a bill, etc.) that something has been received or paid for: *Pay the bill and ask the grocer to receipt it.* **3.** receiving; being received: *On receipt of the news she burst into tears.*

ref er ence (ref′ər əns), **1.** direction of the attention: *In his speech he made many references to a famous author.* **2.** mention: *Do not make any reference to his lameness.*

re frig er ate (ri frij′ər āt), make or keep cool or cold.

re fund (ri fund′ for 1, rē′fund for 2), **1.** pay back: *If these shoes do not wear well, the shop will refund your money.* **2.** return of money paid.

reg is ter (rej′is tər), **1.** a list; record. **2.** book in which a list is kept. **3.** write in a list: *Register the names of the new pupils.* **4.** thing that records. A cash register shows the amount of money taken in. **5.** indicate; record: *The thermometer registers 90 degrees.* **6.** an opening with an arrangement to control the amount of air or heat that passes through.

reign (rān), **1.** the period of power of a ruler: *The queen's reign lasted many years.* **2.** to rule. **3.** exist in many places; prevail: *On a still night silence reigns.*

rel a tive (rel′ə tiv), **1.** father, sister, aunt, cousin, etc. **2.** having a connection with each other: *John considered the relative merits of the two books before buying one of them.* **3. Relative to** means (1) about; concerning. (2) in proportion to.

re li a ble (ri lī′ə bəl), worthy of trust; that can be depended on: *Send Joe to the bank for the money; he is a reliable boy.*

re luc tant (ri luk′tənt), unwilling; slow to act because unwilling: *The policeman led the reluctant boy to the principal. I am reluctant to see the summer end.*

re mote (ri mōt′), **1.** far away; far off: *The North Pole is a remote part of the world.* **2.** distant: *He is a remote cousin.* **3.** slight: *I haven't the remotest idea what you mean.*

re sign (ri zīn′), **1.** give up; give up a job, office, etc.: *The manager of the football team resigned because of illness.* **2.** give up; submit: *Jim had to resign himself to a week in bed when he hurt his back.*

re sort (ri zôrt′), **1.** go; go often: *Many people resort to the beaches in hot weather.* **2.** place people go to: *There are many summer resorts in the mountains.* **3.** turn for help: *The spoiled child resorted to tears to get her way.*

re tire (ri tīr′), **1.** give up an office, occupation, etc.: *My father intends to retire at 65.* **2.** go away to be quiet: *The author retired to the country to finish his book.* **3.** go back; retreat: *The soldiers retired in good order.* **4.** go to bed: *We all retired early.*

Re vere (ri vēr′), **Paul,** American patriot (1735-1818) noted for his ride to give warning of the coming of the British troops.

re vive (ri vīv′), **1.** bring back or come back to life or consciousness: *to revive a half-drowned person.* **2.** come back to a fresh, lively condition: *Flowers revive in water.* **3.** restore; make fresh: *Hot coffee revives a cold, tired man.*

rev o lu tion (rev′ə lü′shən), **1.** a complete overthrow of an established government. The American Revolution (1775-1783) gave independence to the colonies. **2.** complete change: *The automobile caused a revolution in ways of traveling.* **3.** a moving round some point in a circle or curve: *One revolution of the earth around the sun takes a year.* **4.** turning round: *The revolution of the earth causes day and night.*

rheu ma tism (rü′mə tiz əm), disease with soreness, swelling, and stiffness of the joints.

rhythm (ri™′əm), **1.** movement with a regular repeating of a beat, accent, rise and fall, or the like: *the rhythm of music or dancing, the rhythm of the tides.* **2.** the repeating of an accent; the arrangement of beats in a line of poetry.

rind (rīnd), firm outer covering. We do not usually eat the rind of oranges or cheese.

rock er y (rok′ər i), garden with flowers planted among rocks.

route (rüt or rout), **1.** way to go; road: *Shall you go by the northern route?* **2.** send by a certain route.

rou tine (rü tēn′), **1.** fixed, regular way of doing things; the doing of the same things in the same way by habit: *Getting up and going to bed are parts of your daily routine.* **2.** using routine: *routine workers.*

rue ful (rü′fəl), sorrowful; unhappy; mournful: *a rueful expression.*

---

hat, āge, cãre, fär; let, ēqual, tèrm; it, īce; hot, ōpen, ôrder; oil, out; cup, pùt, rüle, ūse; ch, child; ng, long; sh, she; th, thin; ™, then; zh, measure; ə represents *a* in about, *e* in taken, *i* in pencil, *o* in lemon, *u* in circus.

ru mor (rü′mər), **1.** story or statement talked of as news without any proof that it is true: *The rumor spread that a new school would be built here.* **2.** vague, general talk: *Rumor said that the two countries would soon come to an agreement.* **3.** tell or spread by rumor.

Sam ar cand (sam′ər kand or sam′-ər kand′),   city in western Asia. Also **Samarkand.**

Sche nec ta dy (skə nek′tə di), city in eastern New York State.

schol ar (skol′ər), **1.** learned person; person having much knowledge. **2.** pupil at school.

scut tle[1] (skut′əl), a kind of bucket for holding or carrying coal.

scut tle[2] (skut′əl), scamper; scurry: *At their master's command, the dogs scuttled off into the woods.*

seam (sēm), **1.** the line formed by sewing two pieces of cloth, canvas, leather, etc., together: *the seams of a coat, seams of a sail.* **2.** any line where the edges join: *The seams of the boat must be filled in if they leak.* **3.** mark (the face, etc.) with wrinkles, scars, etc. **4.** layer: *a seam of coal.*

Se at tle (si at′əl),   seaport city in Washington State.

Se lim (sē′lim).

sem a phore (sem′ə fôr), **1.** apparatus for signaling; upright post or structure that has movable arms, an arrangement of lanterns, flags, etc., used in railroad signaling. **2.** to signal by semaphore.

RED LIGHT   YELLOW LIGHT   GREEN LIGHT

STOP   CAUTION   PROCEED

Railroad semaphores

ses sion (sesh′ən), **1.** a sitting or meeting of a court or some special group. **In session** means meeting: *The court is now in session.* **2.** a single, continuous course or period of lessons, such as morning and afternoon school sessions.

shaft[1] (shaft), **1.** long, slender part or piece, such as the stem of a spear, an arrow, etc. **2.** one of the two wooden poles between which a horse is harnessed to a carriage, etc.

shaft[2] (shaft), **1.** deep passage sunk in the earth. The entrance to a mine is called a shaft. **2.** long, narrow space: *an elevator shaft.*

sheer (shēr), **1.** very thin: *She wore a sheer white dress.* **2.** complete: *The girl fainted from sheer weariness.* **3.** straight up and down; steep: *From the top of the wall there was a sheer drop of 100 feet to the water below.*

shift (shift), **1.** change from one place, position, person, etc., to another; to change: *He shifted the suitcase from one hand to the other. The wind has shifted to the southeast.* **2.** a change; a substituting in the place of another person or thing: *There are two shifts of work in the factory.* **3.** group of workmen; group: *This man is on the night shift.* **4.** manage to get along. **Shift for oneself** means get along by one's own efforts.

shil ling (shil′ing),   British coin worth about 14 cents in United States money (1955).

Si er ra Ne vad a (si er′ə nə-vad′ə or si er′ə nə vä′də), mountain range in eastern California.

sil hou ette (sil′ü et′), **1.** outline portrait cut out of black paper or filled in with a single color. **2. In silhouette** means shown in outline, or in black against a white background. **3.** show in outline: *The mountain was silhouetted against the sky.*

si moom (sə müm′), hot, sand-laden wind of the deserts of Arabia, Syria, and northern Africa. Also **simoon.**

smol der (smōl′dər), burn and smoke without flame: *the smoldering ashes of a fire.*

smug (smug),   self-satisfied; too pleased with one's own goodness, cleverness, etc.

snare drum (snãr drum), small drum with strings stretched across the bottom to make a rattling sound.

Bottom of snare drum

snub (snub),   **1.** treat coldly, scornfully, or with contempt. **2.** check or stop (a boat or a horse) suddenly. **3.** short and turned up at the tip: *a snub nose.*

spat ter dash (spat′ər dash′), long legging or gaiter worn to keep the trousers or stockings from being splashed with mud, etc. Usually, **spatterdashes.**

spav in (spav′ən),   disease of horses in which a bony swelling forms at the leg joint, causing lameness.

spec ta cle (spek′tə kəl),   **1.** thing to look at; sight. **2.** public show or display: *A big army parade is a fine spectacle.*

spec ta cles (spek′tə kəlz),   pair of glasses to help a person's sight or to protect his eyes.

speed om e ter (spēd om′ə tər), instrument to indicate speed.

spon sor (spon′sər),   **1.** person who is responsible for a person or thing: *the sponsor of a law.* **2.** act as sponsor for.

squire (skwīr),   **1.** in England, a chief landowner in a district. **2.** in the United States, a justice of the peace or a local judge.

stake[1] (stāk),   **1.** a stick or post pointed at one end for driving into the ground. **2.** mark with stakes; mark the boundaries of: *The miner staked off his claims.*

stake[2] (stāk),   **1.** risk (money or something valuable) on the result of a game or on any chance: *He staked his money on the black horse.* **2.** the money risked; what is staked. He has much **at stake** means he has much to win or lose. **3.** something to gain or lose; an interest; a share in a property: *Each of us has a stake in the future of our country.*

star board (stär′bərd),   the right side of a ship, looking forward.

states man (stāts′mən),   man skilled in the management of public or national affairs.

sti fle (stī′fəl),   **1.** stop the breath of; smother: *The smoke stifled the firemen.*   **2.** be unable to breathe freely: *I am stifling in this close room.*   **3.** stop; keep back: *to stifle a cry, to stifle a yawn.*

sub way (sub′wā′),   **1.** underground passage. **2.** underground electric railroad.

suf fi cient (sə fish′ənt),   enough; as much as is needed.

Su lie man (sü′lē män).

sul phur (sul′fər),   light-yellow substance that burns with a blue flame and a stifling odor. Sulphur is used in making matches and gunpowder. Also **sulfur.**

sun di al (sun′dī′əl),   instrument for telling the time of day by the position of a shadow cast by the sun.

Sundial

su pe ri or (sə pēr′i ər),   **1.** better; higher; greater: *Our army fought off a superior force.* **2.** showing a feeling of being above others; proud: *The other girls disliked Ann's superior manner.*

su pe ri or i ty (sə pēr′i ôr′ə ti), superior state or quality: *No one doubts the superiority of modern ways of traveling over those of olden times.*

---

hat, āge, cãre, fär; let, ēqual, tėrm; it, īce; hot, ōpen, ôrder; oil, out; cup, pùt, rüle, ūse; ch, child; ng, long; sh, she; th, thin; ₮H, then; zh, measure; ə represents *a* in about, *e* in taken, *i* in pencil, *o* in lemon, *u* in circus.

311

su per sti tion (sü′pər stish′ən),
belief or practice founded on fear or
ignorance.

surge (sėrj),   **1.** rise and fall; move
like waves: *A great wave surged over
us.*   **2.** a wave; a sweep or rush of
waves.   **3.** something like a wave: *A
surge of anger rushed over him.*

sus pend (səs pend′),   **1.** hang down
by attaching to something above: *The
lamp was suspended from the ceiling.*
2. stop for a while: *Building operations were suspended during the winter.*
3. remove or exclude for a while
from some privilege or job: *William
was suspended from school for a week
for bad conduct.*

sus pense (səs pens′),   **1.** condition
of being uncertain: *This detective story
keeps you in suspense till the last page.*
2. anxious uncertainty; anxiety.

sym pa thet ic (sim′pə thet′ik),
1. sharing another's feelings.   **2.** ap-
proving; agreeing.   **3.** enjoying the
same things and getting along well
together.

sym pa thet i cal ly (sim′pə thet′-
ik li),   in a sympathetic manner;
with sympathy.

tank ard (tangk′ərd),
large drinking mug with
a handle and hinged cover.
See the picture.

ten sion (ten′shən),
1. stretching.   **2.** stretched
condition: *The tension of
the bow gives speed to the*   Tankard
arrow.   **3.** strain: *A mother
feels tension when her baby is sick.*

term (tėrm),   **1.** word or group of
words used in connection with some
special subject: *television terms;
railroad terms.*   **2.** name; call: *He
might be termed handsome.*   **3.** a set
time; length of time: *The President's
term of office is four years. Schools
usually have a fall term and a spring
term.*

ter mi nal (tėr′mə nəl),   **1.** at the
end; forming the end. Terminal buds
grow at the end of stems.   **2.** the end.
A railroad terminal is the station,
sheds, tracks, etc., at either end of
the line.

tour (tür),   **1.** travel from place to
place.   **2.** travel through: *Last year
they toured Mexico.*   **3.** a journey: *a
European tour.*   **4.** walk around: *The
children made a tour of the ship.*

trac tion (trak′shən),   **1.** drawing
or pulling; being drawn.   **2.** the drawing or pulling of loads along a road,
track, etc.   **3.** kind of power used for
this. Electric traction is used on
parts of some railroads.   **4.** friction:
*Wheels slip on ice because there is too
little traction.*

trance (trans),   **1.** state or condition somewhat like sleep, in which
the mind seems to have left the body.
2. dreamy or absorbed condition: *The
old man sat before the fire in a trance,
thinking of his past life.*

trea son (trē′zən),   falseness to
one's country or to one's king.
Helping the enemies of one's country
is treason.

trib ute (trib′ūt),   **1.** money paid
by one nation to another for peace
or protection or because of some
agreement.   **2.** any forced payment.
3. expression of thanks or respect:
*The loud applause was a tribute to
the actor's fine performance.*

tril li um (tril′i əm),   a plant with
three leaves around a single flower.

tri o (trē′ō),   **1.** piece of music for
three voices or instruments.   **2.** three
singers or players.   **3.** any group of
three.

u nan i mous ly (ū nan′ə məs li),
with complete agreement; without a
single opposing vote.

un can ny (un kan′i),   strange and
mysterious; weird: *The trees took
uncanny shapes in the half darkness.*

312

un par al leled (un par′ə leld), un-
equaled; matchless; having no parallel.

un seem ly (un sēm′li), improper;
not suitable: *Laughing in church is
unseemly.*

valve (valv), movable part that
controls the flow of a liquid or gas
through a pipe by opening and
closing the passage. A faucet is one
kind of valve.

vein (vān), **1.** one
of the blood vessels
or tubes that carry
blood to the heart
from all parts of the
body. **2.** rib of a
leaf or of an insect's
wing. **3.** a crack or
seam in rock filled
with a different mineral: *a vein of
copper.*

Veins: A, of leaf;
B, of insect's
wing.

ver ti cal (vėr′tə kəl), straight up
and down: *A person standing up
straight is in a vertical position.* See
the picture for **horizontal**.

ves try (ves′tri), room in a church
where meetings are held, supplies
kept, etc.

vet (vet), short form of **veterinar-
ian.** *Used in common talk.*

vi brate (vī′brāt), **1.** move rapidly
to and fro: *A piano string vibrates
and makes a sound when a key is struck.*
2. quiver; be moved.

vig or ous (vig′ər əs), strong and
active; energetic; forceful.

vis i bil i ty (viz′ə bil′ə ti), **1.** condition or quality of being visible:
In a fog the visibility is very poor.
2. the distance at which things are
visible.

vi tal (vī′təl), **1.** necessary to life:
The heart is a vital organ. **2.** very
necessary; very important: *Providing*
*enough schools for children is a vital
problem.* **3.** Causing death, failure, or
ruin: *a vital wound, a vital blow to
an industry.*

vi zier or **vi zir** (vi zēr′), high
official in Mohammedan countries;
minister of state.

volt age (vōl′tij), electrical force
expressed in volts. A current of high
voltage is used in transmitting electric power over long distances.

war i ly (wãr′ə li), in a wary manner; cautiously.

war y (wãr′i), **1.** on one's guard
against danger. **2.** cautious; careful.

weird (wērd), unearthly; wild;
mysterious; strange: *The witches
moved in a weird dance.*

wheeze (hwēz), **1.** breathe with
difficulty and with a whistling sound.
2. whistling sound caused by difficult
breathing. **3.** make a sound like this:
The old engine wheezed.

Xen o phon (zen′ə fən).

yon der (yon′dər), over there;
within sight, but not near: *Look at
that wild duck yonder!*

Ys o bel (ē′sə bel or iz′ə bel).

zone (zōn), **1.** any of the five great
divisions of the earth's surface,
bounded by lines parallel to the
equator. **2.** any region or area especially considered or set off. A war
zone is a district where fighting is
going on. **3.** in the United States
parcel-post system, an area to all
points within which the same rate
of postage is charged for parcel-post
shipments from a particular place.
4. divide into zones: *The city was
zoned for factories and houses.*

---

hat, āge, cãre, fär; let, ēqual, tėrm; it, īce; hot, ōpen, ôrder; oil, out; cup,
pùt, rüle, ūse; ch, child; ng, long; sh, she; th, thin; ŦH, then; zh, measure;
ə represents *a* in about, *e* in taken, *i* in pencil, *o* in lemon, *u* in circus.

TO THE TEACHER

The new *People and Progress*, Book 6[1], with its accompanying *Guidebook* and *Think-and-Do Book*, continues The New Basic Reading Program for the middle grades. It is designed for approximately one semester's use whenever the child has successfully completed *More Days and Deeds*.

The new *People and Progress* contains 657 words not introduced by the end of Book 5[2] of The New Basic Reading Program. In the first unit of the new *People and Progress*, no page introduces more than five new words, and no page in the entire book introduces more than six new words.

The 657 new words in this book are shown in the vocabulary list below. The following forms of known words are not counted as new (including those forms made by changing *y* to *i* or *f* to *v*, by dropping the final *e*, or by doubling the final consonant in the root word): forms made by adding or dropping the inflectional endings *s*, *es*, *ed*, *ing*, *n*, *en*, and *er*, *est* of comparison; possessives; forms made by adding or dropping the prefixes *dis-*, *fore-*, *im-*, *re-*, or *un-*, and the suffixes *-able*, *-al*, *-en*, *-er*, *-ful*, *-ish*, *-less*, *-ly*, *-ment*, *-ness*, *-or*, *-ous*, *-ship*, *-ward*, or *-y*, and *-teen*, *-th*, or *-ty* of numerals; compounds made up of known words; common contractions. Homographs are not counted as separate words; for example, if *scuttle* meaning "to scamper or scurry" has been introduced, *scuttle* meaning "a kind of bucket for holding or carrying coal" is not counted as a separate word. Nonsense words, syllables that represent sounds, and the following foreign words are not counted: *dinar*, *bismillah*, *hu akbar*.

Boys and girls can attack independently all of the 657 new words by applying the word-analysis and dictionary skills developed in The New Basic Reading Program. The words printed in italics in the vocabulary list are those that are included in the glossary of the new *People and Progress*.

VOCABULARY LIST

UNIT I

6 *Revere*
  Nelson
7 historical
  character
8 *critically*
  route
  boosted
9 wig
10 *principal*
  jogged

column
blared
11 habit
  patience
  gritted
12 *quivered*
  siren
13 *ranks*
14 *intense*
  wheezed
  hero

15 scuffed
  reluctantly
  botany
  apartment
  fumes
16 *subway*
  Evelyn
  Jessie
  altogether
17 organize

18 *trilliums*
  chewink
  automatically
  bashfully
19 *columbines*
  sassafras
20 . . . . .
21 contradicted
22 garter
  flushed
  foliage

314

23 . . . . .
24 admiration
identify
ouch
gurgling
25 . . . . .
26 *heroine*
27 *bulletin*
science
28 Clinton
compete
cinch
demons
29 propped
February
30 *gloats*
guarantee
aside
31 responsible
stake
boo
32 whittle
Dana
pencil
33 gym
34 *congratulated*
contestant
35 Jenkins
Centerville
skeleton
ghostly
36 *suspended*
draft
carved
Claude
Spencer
37 *huckleberries*
omitted
Stan
38 *smugly*
39 *weird*
twigs
40 *collided*
pell-mell

41 racket
conspirators
failure
unanimously
42 smudge
43 piano
devote
vigorously
Victor
44 *genius*
orchestra
clarinet
achieve
45 *composition*
rhythm
assembly
term
Thorpe
46 gong
register
47 . . . . .
48 . . . . .
49 . . . . .
50 explosion
51 *snare*
energetic
52 *tribute*
medal
53 . . . . .
54 . . . . .
55 . . . . .
56 braked
57 Derby
Brad
Akron
Gram
58 expenses
dialed
sympathetically
Pidge
pinch
59 reserved
60 local
consent
sponsored

61 *dawdled*
62 grudge
63 . . . . .
64 tattler
photographers
65 *Seattle*
Steve
66 *surge*
67 *captive*
Clyde
impact
68 tensed
snub
69 . . . . .
70 *process*
71 defiantly
72 memory
affected
famished
definitely
73 . . . . .
74 pursuit
shaft
75 . . . . .
76 rotten
shift
extent
77 possibility
hampered
clogged
ounce
78 *stifled*
staggered
79 *jeep*
pajamas
80 *warily*

UNIT II

82 January
Lovelace
83 *notion*

84 *public*
85 *Meriden*
86 healthy
groomed
87 bidding
farewell
brimming
88 *derived*
parcel
89 *penetrated*
miracle
90 *relatives*
91 . . . . .
92 Harlem
raft
Manhattan
colonies
beckoned
93 . . . . .
94 *Gazette*
Timothy
editor
contract
95 Nellie
convention
Philadelphia
96 *declaration*
scissors
delegates
independent
treason
revolution
97 *reliable*
suspense
Jip
Jenny
98 biscuits
99 *patriot*
trampling
100 *revived*
uncanny
101 item
moreover
heir

102 *Albany*
Derek
Dexter
DeWitt
Schenectady
103 locomotive
draped
tour
104 *yonder*
dignified
105 bonnets
gestured
tension
terrific
106 fiery
jets
crimson
smoldered
diminished
107 applied
performance
108 balked
convulsively
worst
cured
chugged
triumphantly
109 absence
ma'am
deacon
hotel
gingerbread
110 *silhouette*
111 *exposition*
Corliss
machinery
Lucy
contraption
112 *centennial*
affair
postponed
113 fountains
million

114 *innumerable*
115 *demonstrated*
116 *trance*
117 pistons
labeled
consisted
horizontal
pedals
118 Humber's
spider
119 . . . . .
120 *newfangled*
Nan
Marshall
booth
stitches
Jimmie
121 . . . . .
122 . . . . .
123 *implored*
124 *gingerly*
125 *ruefully*
posthaste
century
126 . . . . .
127 . . . . .
128 elm
livery
129 riddle
bureau
mackintoshes
130 . . . . .
131 Terry
Randall
Kokomo
Haynes
132 Atlantic
retired
Apperson
limits
ingenuity
patriotic

133 *mildly*
Paris
134 *Michigan*
Hollins
No.
dray
gears
traction
135 *ancestors*
136 *deputy*
inalienable
liberty
137 *fogies*
perspiration
authority
138 sentence
twirl
139 . . . . .
140 poetry
Godlike
stylish
accomplishment
141 . . . . .
142 . . . . .
143 earphones
Peggy
chimed
144 *Marconi*
Italy
Morse
Daisy
145 *rumor*
Brant
146 parlor
strung
cranberries
147 *aghast*
148 Mars
149 . . . . .
150 carols
151 holy
152 . . . . .

UNIT III

154 *trio*
cue
strumming
chords
guitar
accordion
155 audition
mellow
nevertheless
session
sufficient
merit
156 sung
muff
gust
157 . . . . .
158 depressed
159 disclosing
reels
device
phonograph
160 dubbed
consulting
apparatus
161 plugging
outlet
melody
162 . . . . .
163 blurring
164 . . . . .
165 situation
available
166 momentary
sensation
rhythmic
relieved
167 . . . . .
168 Brewster
spine
starboard
lieutenant
Sprong
Hudson

316

317

ILLUSTRATIONS

The pictures in this book were made by Joseph Pearson (cover, pp. 1, 5, 81, 153, 219); Jack White (pp. 2-3, 6-80); Henry M. Picken (pp. 82-93, 111-118, 143-151, 154-166, 174-185); Rafaello Busoni (pp. 94-101); David Hendrickson (pp. 102-110, 120-142); John Merryweather (pp. 167-168, 171, 196-197, 206-218, 270-284); Harve Stein (p. 170); Seymour Fleishman (pp. 186-195); Clifford Schule (pp. 198-205); Constance Moran (pp. 220-229, 246-247, 268-269); Charlotte Becker (pp. 230-243, 248-256); Hugh Lofting (pp. 257-267); Bruno Frost (pp. 285-295).

ACKNOWLEDGMENTS

For permission to adapt and use copyrighted material, grateful acknowledgment is made to the following:

To the publishers for "Paul Revere Rides Again" by Jack Bechdolt, copyright, 1951, by Story Parade, Inc., reprinted by permission; to the author and publishers for "Turn About" from "Nancy" by Eleanor Clymer in *Girls Today;* to the author and publishers for "Dark Horse" by Custer Clark in *Boys Today;* to Mrs. Graham Doar and to the publishers for "Who's Scared of Bears?" by Eleanor Hammond in *Wee Wisdom;* to the publishers for "Martha Wasn't Musical" by Adelia Macmillan, copyright, 1945, by Story Parade, Inc., reprinted by permission; to the author and publishers for "Every Time I Climb a Tree" from *Far and Few* by David McCord, by permission of Little, Brown & Company; to the author and publishers for "Cheers for the Winner" by Florence M. Davis in *Wee Wisdom;* to the author and publishers for "The Captive" by William L. Jackson in *Boys Today.*

To the author for "Sent by Mail" by Jean Mathias; to the author for "News for the Gazette" from "Timothy's Ride" by Frances Cavanah; to the author for "All Aboard!" by Jeannette Covert Nolan in *Child Life;* to the author and publishers for "Farewell to the Boneshaker" from "Boneshaker's Farewell" by Elsie Singmaster in *Boys Today;* to the publishers for "The Horseless Carriage" from "Terry Randall Goes Riding," reprinted by permission of Dodd, Mead & Company from *America Was Like This* by Emma Gelders Sterne, copyright, 1941, by Dodd, Mead & Company, Inc.; to the author for "From out the Christmas Skies" by Marion Barrett Obermeyer.

To the author for "Trials of a Trio" by Ruth Stempel; to the author for "Coast Guard to the Rescue" from *Air Patrol* by Henry B. Lent; to the author for "Telephone in Motion" by Ellen MacGregor; to the author for "Signals for Safety" by Anton H. Remenih; to the author for "Expert Shovelman" by Fred D. Berkebile; to the author and publisher for "Crop Duster" by Joseph Stocker in *Boys Today.*

To the publishers for "The Caliph's Clock" from *The Pigtail of Ah Lee Ben Loo* by John Bennett, copyright, 1928, by Longmans, Green and Co., Inc.; to the publishers for "Rhyming Ink," reprinted by permission of Dodd, Mead & Company from *Fifteen Tales for Lively Children* by Margaret and Mary Baker, copyright, 1939, by Dodd, Mead & Company, Inc.; to the publishers for *Ben and Me* by Robert Lawson, reprinted by permission of Little, Brown & Company.